Mills & Boon
Best Seller Romance

A chance to read and collect some of the best-loved novels from Mills & Boon—the world's largest publisher of romantic fiction.

Every month, six titles by favourite Mills & Boon authors will be re-published in the *Best Seller Romance* series.

A list of other titles in the *Best Seller Romance* series can be found at the end of this book.

RACHEL LINDSAY
SECRETARY WIFE

MILLS & BOON LIMITED
LONDON · TORONTO

First published 1976
Australian copyright 1983
Philippine copyright 1983
This edition 1983

© Rachel Lindsay 1976

ISBN 0 263 74259 8

Set in Linotype Baskerville 11 on 11½ pt.
02–0483

Made and printed in Great Britain by
Richard Clay (The Chaucer Press) Ltd,
Bungay, Suffolk

CHAPTER ONE

LAURA PEARSON finished the last line of the letter she was typing, pulled it from the machine and set it on the large pile that lay beside her desk. Only when this had been done did she glance at her watch. A quarter to four. Mr Anderson should have left the airport by now and be on his way to London.

From somewhere in the distance came the sound of a hammer as one of the office boys fixed a Welcome Home banner across the downstairs foyer. She herself had not made any preparations to greet him, knowing that although he would appreciate the pleasure shown by the rest of his staff, he would expect her to be too sensible to bother with such nonsense. Yet how much she would have liked to show her delight at having him back after a two months' absence in Africa.

Two months. It was the longest Carl Anderson had ever been away from the office. Originally he had planned it as a four weeks' trip, but this had soon extended to eight, and had ended with a brief stay in Rhodesia which had not been planned in his itinerary. But now, after thousands of miles of travel, he was coming home.

She jumped up from her desk and went into his office. It was too austere to be called his home, yet this was what it was to him. He had an elegant apartment in an expensive block near Hyde Park, but he used it only to sleep in, preferring to spend his waking hours either here or on the various sites of the buildings he was constructing. She crossed the grey-carpeted floor to his leather-topped desk. How wonderful it would be to come in here and see him sitting behind it in his leather arm-chair, the Venetian blinds partially drawn behind him to monitor the sun, though even the muted rays could not diminish his silver blond head and massive shoulders.

People who saw Carl Anderson for the first time noticed his blondness and size before anything else. Hard on this came awareness of his soft voice and the light-footed way he walked: with the grace of a leopard and the same suggestion of animal strength. Danish by name and parentage, he had been born in England, where both his parents had taught at a south coast university. Despite a reluctance to follow in their academic footsteps, he had nonetheless qualified as an architect, but their death—within a few months of his graduation—had set him morally free and he had decided to travel.

Occasionally he had spoken to Laura of this time in his life, giving the impression that they had been happy years spent in diversified occupations: sheep-farming in New Zealand, opal prospecting in Australia, lumberjacking in Canada. This last job had led to work with a construction company in Banff, where he had soon become foreman and had then been offered the position of manager. Before making up his mind whether or not to settle permanently abroad, he had returned to England for a visit. He had found it small and restricting and was on the verge of leaving when a friend of his from university days, who was now a high-powered tycoon, had asked him to design and build a factory for him. From this had sprung the Anderson Construction Company, and in the eight years since its formation it had become renowned for its high quality work and competitive pricing.

Laura had worked here for five years, the last two as secretary to Carl Anderson. He was an easy employer providing one was totally dedicated to one's work, but he had no patience with anyone who put pleasure before the completion of a job or used the lateness of the hour as an excuse to leave something unfinished. Yet even when he was angry he never lost his temper in a normal way; instead his very quietness could shrivel one's bones. She had personally never experienced his anger, but had seen several members of the staff reduced to pale facsimiles of themselves because of it. But his honesty and integrity—in a profession where such attributes were rare—made people eager to work for him.

The sound of applause told Laura her employer had arrived and she sped back to her desk, forcing herself to remain there when all she longed to do was to rush out and throw herself into his arms. How astonished he would be if she did! She smoothed her hair nervously and clasped her hands in front of her: a picture of the super-efficient secretary he considered her to be.

'Hello, Laura. You don't look as if the strain of managing without me was too much for you.'

Laura blinked her eyes quickly. Carl Anderson had come into the room in his usual quiet way and was standing directly in front of her, as big and broad-shouldered as she remembered, his hair bleached even paler by the tropical sun and his skin so bronzed that his grey eyes looked silver.

'I won't ask if you missed me,' he went on, 'because you look far less harassed than usual!'

'I never look harassed,' she said automatically, and heard him chuckle.

'I knew that would rouse you! You are the calmest secretary I've ever had.'

He went into his office and she followed him, watching as he walked to the centre of the room and stood there breathing in the atmosphere. In some indefinable way he looked different. Perhaps it was because he too looked less harassed. There was a lift to his mouth that suggested happy thoughts and a spring to his step that betokened lightness of mood. He went to his desk and sat down in his chair.

'You don't know how good it is to be back,' he murmured.

Laura sat in front of him: her usual place when she had things to tell him. 'I filed all the letters that arrived in your absence, but I was able to deal with half of them myself. Some I gave to Mr Durban,' she named the Assistant Managing Director, 'but some have had to wait until your return. I'll fetch them for you.' She went to stand, but his hand lifted and stopped her.

'No, Laura, not for the moment.' He leaned his head back against the leather. 'What a taskmistress you are! Don't you realise I've returned home after a long absence and that the prodigal son should be welcomed with a feast, not with work?'

'You've never wanted a feast before!'

'People change,' he said mysteriously.

He lowered his lids and she saw they were dark

with fatigue. Looking at him closely she realised that his tan had fooled her, for the bronze skin around his eyes was marred by wrinkles and a pulse beat noticeably in his left temple—the only sign he ever gave of stress or fatigue. Yet he had broken his return flight for a four-day holiday in Rhodesia. She bit back a sigh. Obviously his rest there had been a frenetic round of amusement.

'I'm engaged to be married, Laura,' he said quietly. 'You're the first person to know.'

Laura's breath caught in her throat and she was glad she was sitting down, otherwise she would have fallen. Even so she could not hide her shock and, seeing it, he smiled.

'I suppose you've always thought of me as too old and wise to succumb to a woman?'

'I've never considered you old,' she said crisply, glad her feelings were well concealed.

'I know it will come as a surprise to everyone.' He was speaking again, more to himself than her, and the smile that turned up the corners of his wide mouth was more pronounced. 'Mind you, it was a surprise to me too. But when you see Rosemary you'll understand why I fell in love with her. She'll be joining me here in a couple of weeks.'

'Joining you?' Laura echoed.

'From Rhodesia. I met her in Cape Town and was with her for most of my trip. It was because of Rosemary that I stopped off in Salisbury. I wanted to meet her parents and persuade them I wasn't too ancient for their daughter.' His smile broadened. 'In the event, they couldn't have been nicer.'

Why shouldn't they be? Laura thought bitterly. What parent would object to a handsome and ex-

9

tremely wealthy son-in-law? And thirty-five wasn't old, despite what he had said about being ancient. She tried to imagine his fiancée, but could not bring an image to mind. Since working for him she had met many of his girl-friends, but meeting one was as good as meeting them all, for they were cast from the same mould: beautiful, sophisticated and brittle. None had remained with him long enough to make any impact on her, though several had tried to enlist her aid in the hope of staying in his life a bit longer. She had been wined and dined in smart restaurants in order to be pumped of all information about him, but had remained her usual diplomatic self and had always returned to the office to tell Carl the outcome of these meetings. Together they would laugh over it and he would instruct her to send the girl an expensive bouquet of flowers as compensation for a meal wasted, and would then regretfully talk of boredom and look through his address book again. Now it seemed there would be no more address book. The unknown Rosemary had, in a matter of weeks, succeeded in capturing a man who had been chased for years by countless women.

'Well, Laura,' he questioned, 'you haven't congratulated me yet. Or does your silence indicate disapproval?'

'It isn't my business to disapprove, Mr Anderson. You merely took me by surprise. Of course I congratulate you.'

'From your frigid tone of voice, you sound as if you're congratulating Rosemary for capturing me!' Laura blushed and his eyes crinkled with amusement. 'I know you're biased in my favour, Laura, but when you meet Rosemary you'll see why she bowled me over.' He swivelled round in his chair

10

and stared through the window at the traffic streaming far below along the grey ribbon roads that wound through Hyde Park. 'For the first time, all the work I've done, every effort I've made, seems worthwhile. My life suddenly has a meaning. Can you understand what I'm trying to say?'

She understood him only too well, and was glad he did not understand her in the same way. But then the single-mindedness which he had shown throughout his working life also characterised the way he dealt with his personal one. He had no time to look below the surface of a relationship. If it became too difficult he ended it; if it became too easy, it bored him. Rosemary must be very special indeed if she had made him realise how empty his life had been without her.

'When will you be getting married, Mr Anderson?'

'I want to find a house first. Rosemary wouldn't be happy living in an apartment. She's used to a big garden and dogs and horses.'

'You'll be looking for somewhere in the country, then?'

'That would be ideal, but unfortunately it isn't practical. I'll get a place in the country for weekends, but the first thing is to find a town house. I thought of Dulwich or Highgate—somewhere within half an hour of here. I'll give you all the requirements and you can get on to it right away.'

'Wouldn't your fiancée prefer to do her own house-hunting?' Laura asked.

'She doesn't know London and she's more than happy to leave it to me. And I'm happy to leave it to you!' He turned from the window and gave Laura a singularly sweet smile. 'I have no hesitation in relying on your judgment.'

With a murmur of thanks she stood up. 'If you don't want to do any work, I suggest you give me the particulars of the house. Then I can start telephoning the agents.'

The speed with which he rattled off the size, situation and type of house he wanted showed he had given it a great deal of thought, and she could not stop a spasm of jealousy. Hard on this came a deep shame for allowing her emotions to get the better of her. Carl Anderson had never, by word or gesture, led her to believe she meant anything more to him than a highly prized secretary, and she had only herself to blame for falling in love with him.

To begin with, his numerous affairs had caused her a great deal of misery, but as one girl followed another, she became used to his flirtations and eventually reached the stage where she was indifferent to the women who filled his life, finding safety in numbers and pursuing the hope—faint yet always there—that one day he would wake up to the knowledge that the meaningful love for which he was searching was in his own office. Tears of self-pity pricked her eyes and she went quickly to her own office before he saw them.

At Carl Anderson's instigation, Laura handed all her office duties to her own assistant and devoted her days to house-hunting. She had never known there were so many beautiful homes available in London, though each of them seemed to have some flaw that made it unsuitable for her employer's requirements. But ten days after she began her search, she believed she had found the one she wanted, and a phone call to the office brought him immediately to see it.

Confidently she led him from room to room: the two large reception ones which could comfortably hold two hundred people; the smaller library; the morning room and the airy kitchen that not even wooden draining boards and cracked sinks could spoil, and then up the curving flight of stairs to the six main bedrooms that overlooked a two-acre garden and the Heath.

'It all needs a lot of alteration,' he muttered.

'Do you think so?' she asked, deflated.

'Bathrooms for every bedroom,' he explained, 'and a servants' wing above the garage, with its own entrance. And a proper nursery suite, too.' The words must have pleased him, for he repeated them, and Laura turned away to hide her bitterness.

'I'm sorry you don't like the house, Mr Anderson. I will continue to look.'

'Don't be silly, Laura, I like it very much. I never expected to find a house I could just walk into.' He went to the window and looked at the view. 'Rosemary will find this nearly as good as living in the country. I'll build a swimming pool, of course. She's used to an open-air life.'

'She'll find it different from Rhodesia.'

'She has lived here before,' he explained. 'Two years ago she was in London for several months. If I'd met her then, I could have saved myself two years.' He sighed and turned back into the room. 'Not that she would have been ready to settle down then. She's very young, you know. Young and gay.'

'How young?' Laura asked.

'Twenty-three.'

'Oh.'

'What does the "oh" mean?'

'You give the impression that Miss Carlton is a child. Twenty-three isn't all that young.'

'It is to me.'

'I'm only twenty-five,' she replied, and had the satisfaction of seeing him look astonished.

'I thought you were much older.'

'Thanks!'

'No offence,' he said quickly as they walked downstairs to his car. 'Put it down to your super-efficiency and the fact that you never flap when there's an emergency.'

'I have had better compliments in my time!'

He gave her another surprised look and Laura warned herself to guard her tongue; unless she did, he might guess the truth.

'Get in,' he said, opening the car door. 'I'll take you home.'

He had done so many times before when she had worked late for him and, as always when she sat close to him, she was intensely aware of him. He was very much like his car, whose full strength was never fully disclosed though one knew it was there, ready and waiting. He drove with quiet concentration, his lids half lowered, so that one noticed how thick his eyelashes were. Even sitting behind the wheel he looked the six feet three that he was, with the build of an athlete and faintly rugged features: a wide mouth and square jaw, a decisive-looking nose and high forehead. His hands were a surprise, being narrow and long-fingered and as smooth as if they had done no manual work, which she knew was untrue. They were the hands of an artist. She pulled her eyes away from them. The buildings Carl Anderson designed were artistic creations in every sense: exquisite monuments of man's ability to form stone, concrete and glass into glorious shapes.

The car stopped outside the rambling Victorian house where Laura had a small flat.

'Thank you for bringing me home,' she said, getting out of the car.

'Thank you for finding me *my* home,' he replied. 'You must be our first guest.'

With a smile he drove off, and she watched until the car disappeared before she took out her latchkey and opened the front door.

'You must be our first guest.' The words were meant as a gesture of kindness, but they sounded the death knell of her hopes.

Lucky, lucky Rosemary!

CHAPTER TWO

HAVING made up his mind to buy the house, Carl Anderson chafed at the delay in making it his own. He drew up plans for the alterations before its purchase was completed, and Laura marvelled that he felt no obligation to discuss any of them with his fiancée.

'Rosemary is happy to leave everything to me,' he explained when she voiced her fears one afternoon as she went with him to the house to make further notes of all the things he wished done. 'She isn't used to taking responsibility,' he continued. 'She has lived a sheltered life and has always had everything done for her.'

'She'll find it different living here!'

'I hope not. I have an excellent housekeeper who looks after my flat, but I thought of advertising for a married couple as well.'

'You'll need more than a couple to take care of this house,' Laura said, glancing round the huge drawing-room.

'Everything will be as labour-saving as possible: air-conditioning to cut down on the dust; wall-to-wall carpeting in all the upstairs rooms and parquet floors and rugs down here. One should be able to manage with three full-time staff.'

'Are you asking me or telling me?' Laura said so drily that he grinned.

'I suppose I was telling you, but now I think about it, perhaps I'd better ask you!'

'It depends how much Miss Carlton is prepared to do.'

'I don't want her to do anything,' he said instantly. 'She loves riding and swimming and tennis and I don't want her to worry about domestic chores. I'll leave you to work out the staff we need and to find them.'

'There's no point doing that till the house is ready.'

'It will be finished in two months. I'm bringing in a double crew, starting tomorrow.'

'Even before the house is legally yours?'

'I've taken bigger chances than that in my life,' he said crisply, and strode through the downstairs rooms, rattling off a list of things that had to be changed.

Laura's notebook was half full before they finally left the house. As always, the thought of his marriage was uppermost in her mind and she wished that Rosemary Carlton were already here. While the girl remained a shadowy figure it was all too easy to resent her. With her usual logic, Laura knew that only if she liked Carl Anderson's fiancée would she be able to come to terms with his marriage and continue to work for him. Certainly she could not remain in his employ if she went on eating her heart out every time she thought of his future.

Blindly she stared through the window, her mind filled with vivid pictures of the house, occupied and teeming with life; of a joyous Rosemary— young and gay, he had called her—and children sliding down the banisters or running across the lawns. This last thought brought an ache to her chest that made it difficult to swallow. Yes, Carl Anderson would have children and would be a devoted father to them, of that she was sure; as he would also be a devoted husband, provided one knew how to manage him. The thought made her sigh. How easy she herself found it to cope with all his moods; his impatience when work was not going as well as he wanted; his toughness with inefficiency; his dislike of protocol and the mischievous things he did to confound those who practised it; to say nothing of the rare but dangerous occasions when he became silent as a grave and she would sense the explosion bubbling within him. When the eruption came it was always a quiet one, but this made it all the more devastating. Carl Anderson was like an iceberg, she thought suddenly. Only the cool silver tip was visible; the main part of his character lay hidden from sight, its strength only to be guessed at.

'I won't be in the office on Monday,' he announced unexpectedly. 'Rosemary is arriving in the morning and I want to spend the day with her.'

'You have a luncheon with the Board of Directors,' she reminded him, 'and a Board Meeting in the afternoon.'

'Durban can stand in for me.'

'You've never missed a meeting before,' she pointed out.

'I thought you'd be pleased that I intend to take things easier from now on.'

'I'll believe it when it happens!'

'It's happening now,' he said. 'I intend taking more time off and to give Durban greater authority. I have no intention of being the sort of husband who leaves the house at eight in the morning and returns at eight at night.'

Laura said nothing and she was aware of him slowing the car and looking at her. 'I can't make up my mind if you approve or disapprove of what I've said,' he queried.

'Naturally I approve.' She forced warmth into her voice, though hearing his plans filled her with such jealousy that she knew that all the decisions she had made for her own future were valueless. She would never be able to stay with him once he was married. Her nerves were already stretched to breaking point. How much worse it would be when she knew that each night he would leave the office to return to another woman's arms.

'I think you're very wise to want more leisure, Mr Anderson.' Her voice was low and trembling, the words tumbling out one upon the other. 'I feel the same way too. It's a pity to spend all one's time in an office. As a matter of fact I've—I've decided I want to travel—to see more of the world.'

'That's an excellent idea.' He gathered speed and the car moved forward smoothly. 'You have a month's holiday, but there's no reason why we can't make it more. Naturally I'd prefer you to split into two. I don't fancy coping with the office for a six-week stretch!'

'You managed very well before I came to work for you,' she said calmly.

'That was years ago.'

'Only two years, Mr Anderson.'

'It seems more.' There was surprise in his voice.

'Only two years,' she repeated, 'and no one is indispensable.'

He slowed the car again. 'What are you trying to

tell me?'

She did not hesitate, knowing that if she did, she would lose her courage. 'I want to give you my notice. I would like to leave as soon as possible.'

He did not reply, nor did he look at her again. But Laura knew him too well to suppose that his quietness masked indifference. When this big athletic man sat so still and silent it meant his brain was working at full stretch. She wanted to tell him he was wasting his time if he thought he could make her change her mind, but instead she continued to stare through the window, relieved when they finally reached her flat.

Still he said nothing and her hand was on the door when she wondered if he had guessed her real reason for wanting to leave. The thought was enough to send a hot flush of shame coursing through her body, turning her from the composed young woman she always tried to be into an emotionally strung-up girl only a couple of years older than the fiancée whom he regarded as an adorable child to be pampered and cosseted. Bitterness seeped through her all the same, its corrosive quality acting as an abrasive that brushed up her pride and gave her the strength to turn and face him.

'The only time I've been out of England, Mr Anderson, is for a few weeks' holiday in Spain and France. *You* have seen the world and you take it for granted, but for me it's a Mecca, that I must still visit. It would be foolish to wait until I'm too old.'

'You could wait another twenty years and you still wouldn't be old!'

'I don't want to wait twenty years. I want to see life while I'm still young!' She raced on, trying to make herself believe what she was saying, for only then could she convince him. 'You don't know what it's like to sit in an office day after day dealing with the same people, writing the same kind of letters. Your life is varied because each new contract opens up a different situation, but for me it only means the same problems.'

'I thought you enjoyed your work,' he said.

'I do. I enjoy it very much. But I want to do something different. I'm sorry to spring it on you like this, but it just sort of came out.'

'So I see.' His eyebrows lowered, the sleek brown arcs giving a slight shadow to his eyes. 'I owe you an apology, Laura. Because you've always been un-complaining, I assumed you were content to remain with me. That's why I find it hard to envisage the office without you.'

'No one is indispensable, Mr Anderson.'

'You are to me,' he said sincerely. 'Knowing you managed things gave me peace of mind when I was away.

'I'm only your secretary, Mr Anderson. Your business is run by a highly efficient group of directors—Mr Durban, Mr Rogers, Mr Johnson.'

'They help me to manage the business,' he agreed, 'but you help to manage *me*!'

The compliment was unexpected and her throat constricted. How difficult he was making it for her to maintain her position! Yet because she was so moved by what he said, she became more determined not to change her mind.

'I won't insult you by offering you more money,' he said.

'It isn't a question of money.'

'Then how can I persuade you to change your mind?'

21

'You can't. I've given it a great deal of thought and—and I definitely want to leave. Miss Jackson can easily take over from me. She's a bright girl and——'

'Don't sell me Miss Jackson,' he interrupted. 'I'm sure she can cope. It's just that I'm used to *you*.'

Used to you. No words could have more stiffened her resolve to make another life for herself. 'I won't leave you in the lurch,' she said composedly. 'I'll stay until you're married, but I'll leave immediately afterwards.'

'Very well,' he sighed. 'But if you change your mind in the interim, I hope you won't be too proud to tell me?'

'I would never be too proud with you, Mr Anderson,' she lied, and quickly opened the door and ran across the pavement.

Once her decision was made Laura felt more contented. The weeks ahead would be difficult, but knowing they would end with his marriage, she would be better able to cope with them. At least she was limiting the torture instead of facing endless years of living in the background of his life, seeing his happiness but never being able to share it.

As he had indicated, Carl Anderson did not come into the office on Monday and left her to deal with the upheaval this caused. The Board of Directors were disgruntled to find him absent and Jack Durban made a clumsy attempt to pump her for more information about the future Mrs Anderson.

'What's she like, Miss Pearson?'

'I haven't met her yet,' said Laura.

'Surely you've seen a photograph? And doesn't Mr Anderson talk about her? Rhodesian, isn't she?'

'Yes.'

'How old?'

'I don't know.'

He smiled. 'You're a very loyal secretary, Miss Pearson. If Mr Anderson ever shows signs of not appreciating you, I hope you'll know where to come.'

'I'll bear it in mind,' Laura replied evenly, and was thankful when another director approached and she was able to move away.

She did not attend the luncheon, but was present at the Board Meeting which followed. Though the minutes were officially kept by someone else, Laura always made her own notes of what went on. She had begun this by accident a year ago. Sitting in on a discussion her employer was having with a particularly difficult client, she had subsequently given her opinion of what had been said. This had differed from Carl Anderson's own recollection, and though he had been proved right at the time, some months later the client had adopted the policy which Laura had stated he would do.

'But he definitely didn't *say* he would do it,' Carl Anderson had expostulated. 'How did you reach the conclusion that he would?'

'From the way he behaved. He dropped his pen when you mentioned the completion date and he never met your eyes each time he talked about his partner.'

'The psychology of movement,' came the retort. 'You'd better attend all important meetings, Laura, and write down what you see.'

Now her pencil momentarily rested in her lap as Jack Durban read out a boring screed on a contract which had already been agreed. Laura wondered with an imp of mischief how her employer would react if she wrote down the remarks that had been made about him and his fiancée that day. He would only be amused by the curiosity displayed and would not see the antagonism that existed side by side with the affection. Like most high-powered, confident men, he did not realise that his super-efficiency and energy was a source of envy.

It was four o'clock before the meeting ended and she returned to her office. Where was her employer at this moment? Escorting his fiancée around the house he had bought or making love to her in the penthouse suite overlooking Hyde Park, which he had rented for her? Intimate pictures danced before her eyes, making a nonsense of the shorthand she was trying to transcribe. With an exclamation she pulled out the sheet and inserted a fresh one. She must stop thinking like this. Unless she did, she would not be able to continue working for him, and to leave precipitately might make him guess the real reason for her departure.

In desperation she left the office early and went to visit a married girl friend. They had met at secretarial college, though Sheila had soon left to get married. She now had adorable twins and did not regret giving up her career to take care of them, though she always pretended to envy Laura her well-ordered life and the high salary she could spend on herself. Tonight she listened with delight to Laura's decision to leave her job and travel.

'About time too,' was her comment. 'Dick and I thought you were stuck in that job for life.'

'It's a very good job,' Laura protested.

'Marriage is a better one!'

'I knew you'd say that,' Laura smiled. 'Next thing you'll be telling me is that I'm an old maid!'

'You do look a bit prim.' Hands on generous

24

hips, Sheila surveyed her. 'That comes from trying to act Miss Know-All the whole time. You were much gayer before you started working for Wonder Boy Anderson.'

'I was also much poorer,' Laura pointed out.

'In money perhaps—not in spirit.'

'That's why I'm leaving,' Laura said quickly.

'When is he getting married?' asked Sheila.

'It depends when the house is ready.'

'Why can't he live in his flat for the time being?'

'He wants to wait until they can move into the house. He's surprisingly romantic.'

'He sounds besotted,' Sheila said gustily. 'He's treating that girl as if she's made of glass.'

'I think she's happy to leave everything to him.'

'You must tell me what you think of her.'

'I will,' Laura promised, but knew she would have to monitor her opinions lest they give her away. Even Sheila must not be allowed to guess her secret.

'Let's stop talking about Mr Anderson's happy future,' Sheila said, leading the way into the living-room, 'and tell me about yours. Where are you going first? America, Europe, Australia?'

'I don't know. Australia, perhaps. It's a question of where I can get a job.'

'You'll be able to find work anywhere. Good secretaries are at a premium. Anyway, I'm sure Mr Anderson will give you a sensational reference and a pretty hefty cheque too. He'll never find anyone as good as you.'

It was nearly midnight before Laura returned to her flat, which seemed spartan and cheerless after the bustle of the house she had left behind. She slipped off her coat and paused in the centre of the room, a slim girl of medium height, with medium brown hair, medium brown eyes and small, neat features. Nothing to attract one's attention or to excite one's interest, she thought as she saw her reflection in the mirror above the mantelpiece. No wonder Carl Anderson regarded her as a piece of office equipment! And not a complicated one at that, though he kept her well oiled with money and made sure her working conditions were conducive to her giving of her best.

'I'm like an android,' she mused aloud. 'A robot programmed for his needs.' But not for all his needs. The words surfaced to her mind but were not spoken, and with a gasp she ran into her bedroom and began to undress.

Only when she was seen without clothes did something of her real personality emerge. It was apparent in the delicate lines of her body: the small tip-tilted breasts, the narrow waist and softly curving hips, all of which were disguised by the severely tailored blouses and skirts she wore. She donned her nightdress and slipped into bed. It was dangerous to try and change her image now. If she wanted to do it she must wait until she was miles away from London. Yet could a moth become a butterfly when it had remained a moth for so long?

'I'm going to try,' she muttered before she fell asleep, 'even if I only succeed in turning into an ancient butterfly!'

CHAPTER THREE

CARL ANDERSON brought his fiancée to the office the next morning, giving the impression that he was showing them his dearest and most treasured possession. As indeed he was, Laura thought bleakly, taking in a glimpse of china blue eyes and hair no less fair than his own.

Rosemary Carlton fitted her name exactly. She was tall and slender, but not so tall that she did not look fragile and not so slender that she did not have curves. Indeed it was hard to fault her, and a second glance decided Laura that here was a creature on whom the gods had lavished all their gifts. No wonder her employer had been bowled over! She spoke in a light, breathless way that increased her air of fragility and made Laura see why Carl Anderson thought of her as young. Her manner was childlike too, for she had a wide smile and extended both hands in greeting, the slim fingers cool and pink-tipped. She was exquisitely dressed in filmy blue. Not the type of dress in which to visit an office but one which was exactly right for a girl called Rosemary, with her fly-away silvery hair and the huge diamond that sparkled on her left hand, as bright as the shine in her large blue eyes.

'Carl bought it for me yesterday,' she said huskily. 'Isn't it gorgeous? And so is the house,' Rosemary continued before Laura could speak. 'Carl took me to see it yesterday. He said you found it for us.'

'All I did was contact the agents and——'

'Don't devalue what you did,' Carl Anderson interrupted.

He looked happier than Laura had ever seen him, and younger too, in a pale grey suit that drew attention to his eyes. The light-coloured material made him look bigger and he dwarfed his fiancée, who had come to stand beside him, nestling against him like a kitten.

'Don't you think I'm lucky to have found this wonderful man?' Rosemary breathed. 'I still can't believe it.'

'Don't expect Laura to agree with you,' he said. 'Secretaries and valets know all their employers' weaknesses!'

'You don't have any, darling,' his fiancée protested. 'You're perfect.'

'I'll get you to put that in writing,' he replied, and led her into his office.

Forcing her mind to remain blank, Laura blindly sat down at her desk and was still there when her employer came back.

'About those interior decorators I asked you to find for me,' he began.

'I made all the appointments I could.' Laura was glad to be able to concentrate on her notebook. 'Green & Pollock will be here at ten, Mrs Madden at eleven and Wallace Brown at twelve. I didn't make any other arrangements until after lunch as I thought you would prefer to have it alone with Miss Carter.'

'Good thinking,' he smiled. 'I take it these people have already seen the house?'

'Of course. There would be no point in their coming to discuss it otherwise.'

'What would I do without you?' he said sincerely.

'Find someone equally efficient,' she retorted, and heard him laugh before he closed the door behind him.

The last of the interior decorators left at one o'clock, followed almost at once by Carl Anderson and his fiancée, who gave Laura a luminous yet vague smile as she drifted out. He had described her as being sporty, yet she gave the impression of being more like a hothouse flower. A camellia or orchid, Laura concluded, then amended it to a tea-rose. Yes, a tea-rose was an apt description: slender, scented and delicate. 'And I'm a snapdragon,' she thought bleakly, pushing back her chair and reaching for her jacket, more glad than ever that she could start to count her departure in weeks. Six, seven at the most and she would be free to begin her life anew.

At three o'clock Carl Anderson returned to the office alone, saying that Rosemary had a headache and had gone to her hotel to rest. 'How many other decorators do I have to see?' he asked.

'Three.'

'You'd better come and stand in for Rosemary.'

'I don't know her tastes,' Laura protested.

'You're a woman, aren't you?' he smiled. 'You're bound to know more of her likes than I do.' He saw Laura's look of disagreement and added: 'Her taste is exactly the way she looks. Light and delicate. She goes for pastel colours and softness, nothing stark or simplistic.'

Remembering the dramatic yet spartan simplicity of his own apartment, which she had seen when she had gone there to deliver documents for him to sign, she marvelled that he was willing to let his own preferences be completely submerged. She glanced at her book.

'Your first appointment is with a Mrs Eda Foster. She's an American and was highly recommended to me. I'll come in as soon as she arrives.'

'Come in now,' he said. 'I'm tired of seeing you behind your desk.'

Surprised at the comment, she complied, and as she sat down in front of him, he spoke again.

'You haven't reconsidered about leaving me, have you?'

'I'm afraid not.' She did not look at him but knew he was sitting motionless, his hands spread out on the top of his desk. More than any man she knew, he had the ability to relax. Even at times of great pressure she had never seen him smoke or fiddle with his hands. Yet his tension must go somewhere; he would not be human otherwise.

'Where do you intend going?' he asked.

'Australia, I think.'

'Would you like me to introduce you to some of the people I know out there?'

'It would be a great help.'

'Good. I'll give you some letters of introduction and write to a couple of people myself. If you do decide to work for any of them, you'll be able to fill me in on the business scene when I'm in Australia.'

The pleasure his offer had engendered faded into nothing. So he still wanted to utilise her services even when she was no longer working for him! Would he never see her as a young woman with a life of her own outside of business?

'I may not want to do secretarial work once I leave here,' she stated flatly.

'What else can you do?'

'Cook, look after children, keep house.'

'You?'

'I'm quite domesticated, Mr Anderson.'

'I'm sure you are,' he said hastily, 'but I can't see you standing at a kitchen sink.'

'It will probably be a dishwasher!'

Before he could reply, Mrs Eda Foster arrived. She was an ageless American with beautifully coiffured grey hair and shrewd eyes. She had a drawling Southern accent, though there was nothing languid about her manner as she displayed photographs of the houses she had decorated—and then followed this by setting out coloured sketches of the way she envisaged the furnishing of the Hampstead house.

Had it been her decision, Laura would have immediately engaged Mrs Foster, but though she had been told to act on Rosemary's behalf, she had no intention of doing so, and stared poker-faced at the desk.

'What do you think, Laura?' her employer asked.

'What do you think?' she countered.

'There's no point in prevaricating,' Mrs Foster spoke briskly. 'Either you like my style or you don't. I believe in mixing the old and the new. If you want a house that's strictly one period, don't come to me. Kitchens and bathrooms I keep strictly functional, but all other rooms should fit the personality of their owners—not stand out like picture frames.'

'What a marvellous way of putting it,' Laura exclaimed, and then stopped, determined not to give herself away. But she obviously had, for her employer's mouth twitched as he hid a smile. Drat the man for always getting his own way!

'I agree with you, Laura,' he said. 'I don't want a house of any fixed period but a home with character.'

'You'd give character to any home!' Mrs Foster said so promptly that he laughed, showing his strong white teeth.

'How long will it take you to do the job?' he demanded. 'Bearing in mind that I'll be able to expedite delivery of all kitchen and bathroom fixtures.'

'That would speed things up enormously,' Mrs Foster replied. 'Then it will only be a matter of agreeing on colour schemes and fabrics and then deciding on the furniture. I've already seen half the things I would like for the house, so it depends on how much time you and Miss Pearson can give me.' She turned to Laura. 'If you're prepared to hike around London with me five hours a day, I can furnish the house in six weeks. But if I had to bring you the things for approval, it will take twice as long.'

Red-faced, Laura made a disclaiming gesture. 'I'm Mr Anderson's secretary, not his fiancée.'

'My fiancée wasn't well this afternoon,' Carl Anderson said smoothly, 'but I'm sure she'll be delighted to go around with you.' He looked at the sketches again. 'I don't want gold taps and fittings, Mrs Foster, but apart from that, you have *carte blanche*.'

'I get that from all my clients, Mr Anderson.'

He smiled and rose to indicate the end of the meeting. 'I want to make the house a beautiful setting for my wife. If she has any special preferences, please follow them.' He escorted the American to the door. 'You really can get it done in a month?'

Mrs Foster nodded. 'Provided your fiancée does *her* part.'

'Don't worry, she will.'

To begin with, Carl Anderson was proved right. For the first week Rosemary Carlton wandered happily round antique shops and fabric showrooms, but during the second week her interest began to flag and, when she came to the office to wait for her fiancé late one afternoon, she told Laura that she did not have the energy to continue at such a pace.

'The woman's a slavedriver,' she pouted. 'She's at my hotel before I've finished breakfast and we're on the go until five-thirty. Sometimes we don't even stop for lunch!'

'Mr Anderson has given her a deadline,' Laura explained.

'The house won't be much use to me if *I'm* dead!' Rosemary cried. 'Carl has no idea how exhausting it is to rush from shop to shop. My head is simply spinning with colours.'

'I'm sure he wouldn't mind if you told him you wanted to take things more slowly.'

'I daren't do that.' Rosemary looked like a frightened child. 'The poor darling is counting the days until we're married. He'll be heartbroken if it's delayed.'

It was hard for Laura to see Carl Anderson as the eager lover of Rosemary's imagination. In the years she had worked for him she had only known him eager to finish a building ahead of schedule. As for being heartbroken over a woman, the nearest he had come to this had been a passionate pursuit of a new mistress and his abrupt dismissal of her when

33

her sexuality had ceased to excite him. But how different he was when real love came into his life.

'That's why you're the only one who can help,' Rosemary said.

Laura looked up to see pale blue eyes watching her and hastily confessed that her thoughts had been elsewhere.

'I was asking you to go with Mrs. Foster instead of me.'

'Me?' Laura said in surprise.

'Why not? You can do it just as well as I can. All you'd have to remember is that I like soft colours and feminine-looking things.'

'I'm Mr Anderson's secretary,' Laura said crisply. 'I can't take time off to furnish your home.'

'I'm sure Carl will let you go.'

'No!' Laura's voice was high and with an effort she lowered it. 'I wouldn't like to take on such a responsibility, Miss Carlton. It's more than a question of choosing colours. It's——'

'You're frightened!' Rosemary Carlton interrupted, and gave a beaming smile. 'Honestly, Miss Pearson, you have nothing to worry about. Just go around with Mrs Foster and let *her* make the decisions. She knows my taste as well as I do.'

'Then why not let her go alone?'

Rosemary's long lashes lowered. 'Because Carl doesn't want to move into a house that's been furnished by a decorator. He wants it to be *my* taste. And you can stand in for me.'

With a whirl of silken-clad legs the girl disappeared into the inner office. She might be soft and feminine in her appearance, Laura thought wryly, but she had a steamroller's capacity for driving relentlessly over other people's wishes. There was no doubt that Rosemary would make her fiancé do as she wished, and no doubt that she herself would be forced to join Mrs Foster on her daily excursions.

The order came as she was putting the cover over her typewriter, when her employer buzzed her to come into his room. He was behind his desk with Rosemary perched on the arm of his chair, her pale golden head close to his. Laura felt a stab somewhere in the region of her heart and furiously chided herself for behaving like the heroine in a third-rate novel.

'I understand Rosemary has already talked to you about the furnishings?' he said.

'Yes, but I——'

'I'm sure Miss Jackson can manage perfectly well while you're out of the office,' he interrupted. 'You're always telling me how capable she is, and now I'll have the chance of finding out for myself.'

Rosemary Carlton was not the only one with steamroller tactics, Laura thought crossly, and nodded agreement to his suggestion.

'I've left Mrs Foster's home telephone number on the pad,' Rosemary drifted across to the door on a cloud of 'Femme'. 'It will be better if you call her yourself and arrange where to meet her tomorrow morning.' She blew her fiancé a kiss. 'I'll see you at my hotel in an hour, darling. Don't be late.'

She left behind a momentary silence, broken by the man as he leaned forward to sign his mail.

'Mrs Foster is the sort of woman who could tire *me* out, let alone Rosemary,' he murmured. 'It was stupid of me not to realise it. And of course she's not used to making decisions.'

'Nor am I,' Laura said.

Silver grey eyes widened. 'You can't make me believe that!'

'I can make decisions for myself,' she stated, 'but I don't see how I can make them for you and Miss Carlton.'

'Rosemary has enormous trust in your taste.'

'She doesn't know it.'

'She says—and I agree with her—that anyone who had the sense to find Holly Grove has the sense to furnish it.' He signed the last letter and closed the folder. 'There you are, Laura, everything is done. Have a word with Miss Jackson and push off home.'

Laura had no option but to obey and, leaving an ecstatic Miss Jackson—who saw herself elevated to Laura's position ahead of time—she set off for home.

What irony that she should be asked to furnish the house in which Carl Anderson would live with his wife. It would make it doubly difficult for her to forget him when she left. Not only would she have to contend with imagining him making love to Rosemary, she would also know the intimate details of the bedroom in which he was doing it!

With a great deal of trepidation she met Mrs Foster the next day. More quickly than she anticipated, she established a rapport with the woman, and this made it easier for her to reach her decisions on colour and style. The more decisions she made the less aware she became of doing it, and the more distant grew the thought of Rosemary. This was her own home she was decorating; her own bedroom she was helping to prepare; her own kitchen for which she was choosing the newest design in cooker, refrigerator, freezer and washing machine. Only when it came to the question of linen did reality return and, with it, a strong repugnance to make herself responsible for the covers and coverlets that would go on the bridal bed.

'That's something Miss Carlton must do,' she said, her voice ragged.

'I'll have a word with her,' Mrs Foster agreed, the quickness with which she replied making Laura wonder whether she had given herself away to this woman. But if she had, the American was too diplomatic to show it.

At the end of her third week's absence from the office, Laura received a call from Miss Jackson who needed help with a report. It was pleasurably painful to return to familiar surroundings and to know that at any moment the door might open and the man she so desperately longed to see would appear.

'He's working like a demon,' Miss Jackson said. 'He's in the office hours before I arrive. Sometimes I get the impression he's been here half the night.'

'Surely not?' Laura protested.

'He is,' Miss Jackson said vigorously. 'Miss Carlton drops in at all hours and takes him off, and the only way he can catch up with his work is to do it at night. If he doesn't put his foot down with her, she'll send him to an early grave!'

Any belief that Miss Jackson was exaggerating was dispelled by Laura's first glimpse of her employer. He looked ten years older: his eyes red-rimmed and with a crêpy look about the lids; his bronze colour unhealthily yellowed by tiredness. Yet he still exuded the same animal magnetism that always made her weak at the knees.

'Hello, Laura.' His voice was as calm and controlled as ever. 'I'm just off to the Lambeth building site.'

'So I gather.' She eyed his denims and saw him smile.

'You never approve of me when I dress casually,' he commented.

'I don't disapprove of your clothes,' she said at once, 'only of your scrambling all over the scaffolding.'

'I used to be a lumberjack, remember. That's far more dangerous.' He ran his hand over his hair. It needed to be cut, but the extra length made him look even more attractive. 'How are things going with you and Mrs Foster?'

'We've nearly finished.'

'Rosemary is delighted with everything you've chosen.'

'Really?' Laura forbade telling him that his fiancée had not been in touch with Mrs Foster since she had opted out of the daily shopping rounds.

'Yes,' he went on, 'she really loves the house. She's always there.'

'She's always there sunbathing,' Miss Jackson added scathingly when Carl Anderson had left. 'One of the drivers collected parasols and deck-chairs from Harrods and took them up to Hampstead for her. I'm glad we're having a good summer, but sometimes I wish we'd have a cloudburst!'

Thinking of Rosemary sunning herself on a Hampstead lawn while workmen busied themselves in the house behind her and she and Mrs Foster scurried round London and the Home Counties like beavers, Laura echoed the thought, but was too well versed in office diplomacy to give it utterance. 'Miss Carlton is used to a different life from the one we lead,' she placated.

'I'm not knocking the life,' Miss Jackson sniffed,

'merely the way she manages to do it while you do *her* job.'

'Since you're doing mine, I don't see that it matters.'

'Don't you ever get tired of being loyal?' her assistant demanded. 'I'm used to you defending Mr Anderson, but do you have to defend his fiancée too?'

Laura favoured Miss Jackson with a cold stare and wondered whether the girl was suitable to work for Carl Anderson. In his personal life he was not answerable to anyone who worked for him, and if he wanted to make a fool of himself over Rosemary Carlton it was no one's business but his own.

'Give me the report you want me to check for you,' she said. 'I'll do it here and you can return to your own office for the day.'

'Relegated again!' Miss Jackson said.

'Only until I leave permanently.'

'You're definitely going?'

'Definitely,' Laura said, and meant it.

CHAPTER FOUR

LAURA was still working on the report when Carl Anderson returned to the office. There was a faint film of sweat on his face and the red rims round his eyes seemed to have melted into the eyes themselves, making the whites bloodshot.

'You look as if you could do with a bath and bed,' she said crisply.

'I only have time for a shower.' He went through his office to the blue-tiled bathroom that lay beyond it.

It was here that he usually freshened up when he went directly from the office to a dinner engagement, and to this end his valet always saw that his wardrobe here held sufficient clothes and linen. Because of this, Laura was not surprised when he emerged a half-hour later, crisp and clean in a fine wool suit.

'I suppose Miss Jackson made the booking?' he asked and, as Laura looked ignorant, gave a shake of his head. 'I told her to get me a table at the Henley House Club. Rosemary likes dining by the river.'

That explained his rush to leave promptly. He was crazy to be going on an hour's drive out of town when he was so exhausted. 'What about supper at the Griffin?' she suggested, naming a London restaurant famous for its flower-filled terrace and view of Hyde Park.

'Call the Henley House Club and book me a table,' he said in gentle tones, 'and show Miss Carlton in as soon as she arrives.' He retreated into his office, closing the door with a quietness which told Laura he was angry with her for letting him know she was aware of his fatigue.

But why was he ashamed of being tired? And what on earth was the matter with Rosemary that she could not see it for herself? Surely any girl in love with a man would do so. But then Rosemary was not in love with him.

The thought sprang from nowhere and too late, Laura tried to stifle it. But it remained vibrant in her mind. Rosemary did not love Carl Anderson. If she did she would never have wanted him to find a house and buy it without her approval. Nor would she be content to sunbathe her day away while two strange women decorated the home that was going to be hers for the rest of her life. Whatever feelings the girl had for the man whose ring she wore, genuine love was not one of them.

Laura was still trying to absorb these most indigestible thoughts when the originator of them wafted in on a bouquet of musky fragrance. Blue eyes widened as they rested on her and the soft pink lips parted in a charming smile.

'I didn't expect to see you here, Miss Pearson. Don't tell me you and Mrs Foster have finished already?'

'Almost.'

'I adore everything you've chosen. You really are a wonder.'

'I'm glad it meets with your approval. I wasn't sure if you would like blue for the drawing-room.'

'Oh, I do,' Rosemary gushed, and Laura had to forcibly resist reminding her that the final colour scheme chosen was lemon and white.

'Is Carl ready?' Rosemary continued.

'Yes. He's had a very busy day. He only got back a short while ago.'

'Then the sooner I take him from the office the better.'

'Mr Anderson is tired,' Laura blurted out. 'He needs an early night.'

Halfway towards the inner office, Rosemary turned. 'I know exactly what Carl needs. That's why he loves me.'

The door closed behind her, but not before Laura heard the dulcet tones of 'Carl darling' to which, she bleakly thought, Carl darling would suitably respond.

'And now perhaps you'll mind your own business,' she told herself. 'You were annoyed with Miss Jackson for commenting on Carl Anderson's behaviour, and you go and do exactly the same!'

Laura was glad to leave the office and resume her daily rounds of the antique shops. By the end of a further week all the furniture was chosen and only the finalisation of the paint colour for the walls was left to be done. Here too Rosemary wriggled out of all responsibility, complaining that she was allergic to the smell of paint.

'Mr Anderson said *you* would know the colours his fiancée wanted,' the foreman assigned to the house decoration told her. 'If you could spare me some of your time ...'

'I'm entirely at your disposal,' she replied, and proved it by spending several hours with him, going through coloured cards of paint shades.

Leaving a satisfied man to give instructions to his men, Laura returned alone to the room that was going to be Carl Anderson's study. Here she had not taken any notice of Rosemary's preferences for pastels, and had furnished the room in a way she felt fitted the character of its owner. The tall windows would soon be framed by tobacco brown curtains, the floor covered by a Tabriz in variegated golds and reds, and the furniture would be dark and full of lustre, with leather-covered armchairs and a settee capacious enough to suit a wide-shouldered frame. His dressing-room too had been chosen without reference to his bride, and had walnut panelled cupboards, charcoal grey carpeting and a single divan for the nights when he might have a business appointment and return home too late to wish to disturb his wife.

'Not that he'll occupy it often,' Mrs Foster had remarked, making her first and only indiscreet comment. 'I doubt if any woman would find him returning home too late to be welcomed into her bed!'

Laura recalled this comment as she went down the front steps to the drive. The garden was already spruce; the weed-covered lawn replaced by velvet green turf, the bare flower beds filled with bulbs and shrubs that would give colour the year round. The pool was finished too: a blue oasis in a sea of green. Built to Carl Anderson's specifications, it was a testament to the speed with which he could get things done. Even the pavilion that housed the changing rooms stood complete, the entrance to it forming a covered loggia where those who did not like too much sun could relax. A touch of a button would send a glass wall gliding smoothly along its front face, turning it into a hothouse during the winter. To this end the pool was heated, and Laura, coming to the house a few days earlier, had seen it in action, with steam rising from the water.

By the time inclement weather returned again, she would be on the other side of the world, forgotten by the man and woman who would be living here or, at best, remembered as an efficient dogsbody. She knew she was doing her employer an injustice and that he saw her far differently from this, yet she could not prevent these bitter thoughts from erupting, and hoped that time and distance would enable her to see him the way she knew him to be: considerate, intelligent, dynamic—and besotted by another woman.

It was a relief to return to her normal secretarial work. Occasionally Mrs Foster came to the office with a swatch of material or a picture of some extra item of furniture she had found and for which she needed approval, but Laura did not have to return to the house, for which she was grateful.

The wedding date had been set for the end of August. It was going to be a lavish affair with a ceremony in a Mayfair church and a huge reception in a Park Lane hotel. Rosemary had not been too fatigued to rush from shop to shop to buy her trousseau, and Carl Anderson gave Laura a signed cheque book and told her to deal with all the bills. The number of them made her head reel, with many of the dresses costing more than she earned in a month and some costing more than she earned in a quarter, not to mention items like a sable jacket and a mink coat.

'I bought the furs now, darling,' she had heard Rosemary gush, 'because one always gets a bargain in furs in the summer.'

Some bargain, Laura mused, filling out a cheque for two thousand pounds. Still, Carl Anderson could afford it, and if it made him happy ... But would it make him happy? The more she saw of Rosemary, the more disquieted she became. The girl was not only lazy and selfish but she also had a total disregard for anyone else's well-being. Never rising before noon, she would either spend the day in the garden at Holly Grove or expect her fiancé to take her for a three-hour lunch, leaving him at three-thirty to spend a few hours shopping before returning to her hotel to change into one of her new acquisitions and be taken out dining or dancing. These evenings rarely ended before the early hours of the morning, when Carl Anderson would go back to his office to complete the work he had not had time to do during the day. Since he was also trying to deal with many things that would crop up during his month's honeymoon, he had a double work-load to shoulder. But Laura said nothing. She had learned her lesson the first time she had commented on his fatigue and, though her anger smouldered, she kept her silence. More fool him if he wore himself out and left Rosemary a millionaire widow.

A week before the wedding, Rosemary flew to Paris for the final fittings for her bridal gown. Carl Anderson was joining her for the weekend and saw the next few days as ones which would enable him to catch up on all the things still requiring his attention.

'I hope you won't mind working late?' he asked Laura.

Tight-lipped, she nodded.

'Why so sour-faced?' he inquired mildly.

'You don't need me to answer that.'

He hesitated, then smiled. 'No, Laura, I don't.'

That night they did not leave the office until ten, supported by coffee and sandwiches which Laura had provided. As usual he went to drive her home, but she flatly refused to let him.

'Driving you home won't make me any more tired,' he commented.

'No,' she said obstinately, and resolved the argument by hailing a cruising taxi and jumping in.

'You're a bossy young woman,' he teased, standing by the open window. 'I always knew it, but this is the first time you haven't bothered to hide it!'

'Perhaps I'm changing my tactics with you.'

'Then change your mind as well and don't go abroad.'

Her heart pounded violently, but her voice was steady as she spoke. 'I'm afraid my mind is made up on that point. I'm sorry.'

'Not as sorry as I am.' He stepped back, gave the taxi driver a pound note and waved her goodnight.

The glorious summer weather broke next day and, in torrential rain, Laura squelched her way to work. She had slept badly and there was a throbbing in her temples. Slipping out of her sodden shoes and streaming mac, she padded across the room to her desk, almost jumping out of her skin as her employer abruptly emerged from his office.

'I thought you had an appointment in Birmingham,' she gasped.

'I sent Johnson instead. I'm more concerned with the Lambeth scheme. We're running behind schedule and I want to have a look at the site.'

She saw he was wearing his usual working gear of denims and waterproof jacket. 'Don't climb the scaffolding,' she warned. 'It's very slippery under-foot.'

'Yes, mother! You really *are* bossy. Is this your way of trying to make me pleased that you're leaving?'

'You won't even notice I've gone. Everything will be different for you. Your marriage, your home, your secretary. You'll be starting a completely new life.'

'That doesn't mean I have to end the old one——' He paused, as if he wanted to say more. Then he thought better of it and in silence zipped up his jacket and left.

There was a great deal for Laura to do in the office and she began by transcribing some tapes that were too confidential to be done by anyone other than herself. This took a couple of hours and then she busied herself checking a sheet of complicated figures. She was immersed in this when the door burst open and Mr Rogers came in, his face ashen.

'Miss Pearson,' he mumbled.

She jumped to her feet and went towards him. 'Are you ill?'

'No, no, I'm fine. It's——' He sank down on a chair. 'It's Carl.'

Laura's scalp prickled. 'Mr Anderson? What's wrong with him?'

'There's been an accident. He fell . . .'

Laura's knees buckled and she clutched hold of the side of her desk. She tried to speak, but no words came.

'I've warned him a hundred times about climbing the scaffolding the way he does,' Mr Rogers muttered, 'but you know how obstinate he is.'

'Where is he?' Laura finally found her tongue.

'They've taken him to Giles Hospital. Jack Durban has already gone there.' Mr Rogers stood up. 'I said I'd join him.'

'May I come with you?' Laura asked, and though she saw the man's surprise, she stood her ground. 'Mr Anderson may have a message for me—and I——' She stopped, suddenly remembering Rosemary waiting for him to join her tomorrow in Paris. 'I must let Miss Carlton know.'

Mr Rogers groaned. 'She'd better get back fast.'

'Is it that serious?' Laura was still shaking too hard to walk.

'You don't fall twenty feet and just sprain your ankle. All we know is that he's alive.' Mr Rogers went to the door. 'You'd better come with me, then. I don't want to waste time.'

The drive to the hospital seemed interminable, as did the walk down the long corridor of the private wing to a room at the far end, where two doctors stood talking beside the door.

'I'm Dr Marsh,' the younger of the two men said. 'And this is Mr Edwards, the surgeon.' He indicated the sober-looking man beside him. 'Mr Anderson will be taken down to the operating theatre in a few minutes.'

'He's still alive, then?' Mr Rogers asked.

'Just.'

Laura felt the ceiling coming towards her and she leaned against the wall.

'Are you Mrs Anderson?' the doctor asked.

'His secretary,' she whispered. 'How badly is he injured?'

'Both legs are broken and several of his ribs. There are internal injuries, but we won't know how serious they are until we open him up. It was quite

48

a fall, you know. Twenty feet on to concrete. It's a miracle he isn't dead.'

This time Laura could not prevent the ceiling coming down on her and with a moan she crumpled in a faint. She was only unconscious for a few moments, but this mercifully spared her the sight of Carl Anderson being wheeled out of his room to the elevator.

'Can we wait downstairs?' she asked as soon as she was able to speak coherently.

'They don't know how long the operation is going to take,' Mr Rogers said. 'They suggested we went out for lunch.'

Laura almost gagged at the thought and Mr Rogers looked sympathetic. 'I know how you feel, Miss Pearson. *I* can't believe it's happened either.'

She closed her eyes. No words could express the way she felt. Indeed, in an odd way she did not feel anything. She seemed to be suspended above herself, looking down on a man and a girl in a waiting room. It was something she frequently experienced in her dreams. Perhaps this was a dream too. She dug her nails deep into her palms, but though the pain was intense, the dream went on.

'We still have to ring Paris,' Mr Rogers said from a long way off. 'You don't happen to know where Miss Carlton is staying?'

'The Plaza-Athenée. I have the number somewhere.' Laura looked round vaguely.

'Don't worry, the operator will get it for me. I only hope we can contact her.'

He left the room and Laura huddled back in her chair. Time passed, how long she did not know, and Mr Rogers returned.

'I managed to get her,' he said with satisfaction.

'Apparently it's raining cats and dogs there too, so she was lunching in.'

Lunching in bed, Laura thought dispassionately, but managed to take in the fact that Rosemary would be returning on the next available flight.

'You wouldn't care to meet her at the airport?' Mr Rogers asked. 'I'd willingly go myself, but I thought another woman ...'

Laura nodded, although it was the last thing in the world she wanted to do. 'Do you think Miss Carlton would like us to telephone her parents in Salisbury?' she asked.

'She said she'd do it herself. I suppose her father will fly here. What an end to a romance!' He sighed heavily. 'A funeral instead of a wedding.'

'Don't say that!' Laura cried. 'Mr Anderson isn't dead yet.'

'We have to be realistic, Miss Pearson. Even if he comes through the operation, he'll be crippled for life. Don't you think he'd prefer not to wake up from the anaesthetic?'

Laura refused to consider the question. No matter how tenuous Carl Anderson's hold was on life, one must continue to hope and pray he would recover. To this end she clasped her hands together and lowered her head, uncaring what Mr Rogers thought of her action, knowing only that the man she loved must not die.

CHAPTER FIVE

In the event Carl Anderson lived, though in the pain-racked days that followed, he frequently prayed to die.

Laura went each day to the hospital. At first it was only to peep in and see him, drugged and coma-tose, but as the days passed, it was to smile at him and utter brief words of encouragement. Occasion-ally she saw Rosemary Carlton there, but knew, from one of the nurses, that the girl's visits were fleeting.

'She looks like a butterfly and she flits in and out like one,' the nurse said. 'Not that Mr Anderson seems to mind. He's just grateful for any time she spares him.'

Laura, who had become friendly with the nurse, felt no disloyalty in agreeing with her. Mary Roberts was dedicated to her profession and could well be the ideal person to take care of Carl Ander-son when he finally left the hospital. Laura looked at her and decided that now was as good a time as any to ask her if she would be willing to do it.

'Mr Anderson needs a male nurse,' Mary said. 'I can manage him in hospital because there are other nurses to help me, but at home——'

'He has a valet who's willing to do anything that's necessary,' Laura told her.

'It might work,' Mary said cautiously. 'I wouldn't

take it on a permanent basis, though, and he *will* need someone permanently. He'll never walk again.'

'Miracles can happen,' Laura said tremulously.

'The only miracle likely to happen to Mr Anderson is for his fiancée to stay with him.' Mary saw Laura's startled look. 'She won't, you know. She can't bear sickness. I see it in her face when she comes into his room. She won't look at his body even though it's hidden by blankets.'

'He hasn't guessed, has he?'

'It's hard to tell. He isn't a man who gives away his thoughts.'

How well Laura knew this, and hoped she could hide her own feelings equally cleverly. It was becoming increasingly difficult for her to see him each day without giving way to her longing to cradle him in her arms; to give him the reassurance of love that she knew he was longing to hear. But longing to hear it from Rosemary, she reminded herself, not from his secretary. And that was all she was to him: capable, dependable Laura.

'He could lead a normal married life,' Mary said bluntly.

Laura went scarlet and averted her face. 'Does Miss Carlton know?'

'She must do. She had a long talk with the doctor the other day. I think that horrified her even more —to learn that Mr Anderson could be a proper husband. I don't think she'd mind hovering like an angel around his wheelchair, but she doesn't fancy putting herself into his bed!'

Laura remembered this when she went in to see her employer. She had originally intended to see him earlier that day, but a call from Mary had told her that Rosemary was having lunch with him. She wondered if this meant that the girl had decided to do the right thing and remain with him. It was not a difficult decision if one loved the man to whom one was engaged, but impossibly difficult if one were only marrying him for his money. Still, remembering Rosemary's extravagance, she hoped this factor alone would be enough to make her stay with him.

Bracing herself to hear this, she went into his room. She half expected to see a happier look on his face, but he seemed the same as ever and silently held out his hand for the documents she had brought him.

He perused them and made several notes on the side. Only his hands were unchanged since the accident: the nails as well manicured as always, his fingers long and supple. She had always considered them the hands of an artist, and before she could stop herself she blurted out:

'Have you ever painted?'

'In Canada I did a bit. But only because I had to.'

'I meant pictures, not houses,' she said, regretting the question but knowing she had to continue with it. 'I thought it might give you something to do.'

'I have no artistic talent.'

'Matisse didn't think so either. He only started when he was recovering from an operation.'

'Really?' Carl Anderson said indifferently.

'Yes.' She plunged on, determined to make him interested in something. 'He had appendicitis and in those days it took a long time to recover. His mother bought him some paints and a sketching block and he just started.'

'I don't see myself as another Matisse.' More words were scrawled on one of the documents and he handed them all back to her. 'Rosemary has left me. You're the first person to know.'

He spoke in such a matter-of-fact manner that she almost missed what he said. As it was she had to look at him twice to make sure she had heard correctly and, not sure if he was speaking in temporary terms—the girl might have gone to Rhodesia for a holiday or away from London for a few days—she said: 'I understand Miss Carlton had lunch with you today.'

'It was a farewell lunch,' he said calmly. 'Telling me she can't face life with a cripple.'

'Oh no!' Laura caught her breath. 'She couldn't have said that.'

'Not in so many words,' he agreed. 'But the meaning was obvious.' His eyes grew dark with remembered pain and for the first time he showed evidence of feeling. 'I never want to see a woman cry like that again. She desperately wanted to do the right thing, but it was impossible for her. She can't bear sickness. Some people can't, you know. It isn't anything they can help; it just happens. Rosemary hadn't realised she was one of them until I ... until now.'

Laura listened, unable to credit that Carl Anderson should be making excuses for a girl who had let him down so disastrously. Or did he love her so deeply that he did not see her for the selfish person she was?

'You're very forgiving, Mr Anderson,' she murmured.

'If one loves someone, one tries to understand them.' He looked up, his eyes bleak. 'Love doesn't die that quickly, Laura.'

'Miss Carlton's did.'

'Don't say that! Rosemary's young and she'd been cosseted all her life. She——'

'That's no excuse for her to run away when you need her! *You* may delude yourself, Mr Anderson, but I can't.' Laura put the documents in her brief-case. The look on his face told her he was angry, but she had no intention of retracting what she had said. She was glad she had spoken honestly and would have said more had she not been afraid that he had reached the end of his emotional tether.

'I don't know how long you intend to remain in my employ.' He spoke so quietly that she had to strain to hear him. 'But however long you stay with me, you are never to talk of Rosemary in that way again. Do you understand?'

'Yes, Mr Anderson.' She turned the handle and opened the door.

'Laura!'

His voice stopped her, but she refused to turn in case he saw her tears. 'What do you want?' she asked huskily.

'Don't be angry with me. Try to understand how I feel.'

The entreaty in his plea was her undoing, and with a gasp she turned and ran back to his bed, clutching at his hand and dampening it with her tears.

'I don't know how she could bear to leave you,' Laura sobbed, kneeling beside him. '*I* couldn't.'

His free hand came out and patted her shoulder. 'Does that mean you've changed your mind about seeing the world?'

The question checked her tears and her whole

body tensed. She longed to tell him that *he* was her world and that without him in it she would be dead too. But she knew this was the last thing he wanted to hear from her. He needed her as a secretary, as someone to whom he could talk as a friend; never anything more. On a sigh she lifted her head and looked at him, closer to him physically than she had ever been before. How silvery grey his eyes were, and how pale his hair.

'I'll stay with you as long as you need me, Mr Anderson.'

His hand stilled its movement on her shoulder. 'Then you have a job for life, Laura.'

Laura was afraid that Rosemary's departure would affect Carl Anderson's progress. But she had reckoned without his resilience of character. Physically battered he might be, but the will to live was still strong within him, though there were times when she noticed the effort it cost him to conquer his depression.

Respecting his injunction never to be derogatory about Rosemary, she made no mention of her, though coming in to see him unexpectedly one afternoon, she found him staring longingly at the girl's photograph. He made no attempt to hide what he was doing and went on looking at it for several seconds. It was as if he had no pride. He loved Rosemary and he did not care who knew it. It was an honesty Laura admired even as she wished he had the honesty to look clearly at Rosemary's behaviour. If he could admit she was callous and unloving he would be taking the first step towards forgetting her.

Three months after entering hospital, Carl Anderson left it for his home in Hampstead; the home he had lovingly prepared for a wife and in which he would now live alone, apart from his staff.

Several of his fellow directors had tried to persuade him to sell the house and remain in his flat, arguing that for a man in a wheelchair it was a far better solution. But he obstinately refused to consider it, saying it was a beautiful house and that he intended to enjoy it.

Only to Laura was he more expansive, giving practical reasons for his action. 'From now on, my world will be bounded by the four walls where I live, and if my home has a garden and a view I won't feel so restricted. To be confined to a flat would be like living in a coffin. And I'm not dead yet,' he added grimly. 'Not by a long way.'

It was a grey November day when he took up residence at Holly Grove. Laura had visited the house the day before to make sure everything was ready and to personally arrange the masses of flowers that had been sent to him. She also made sure there were the latest magazines and business journals in the library, a plentiful supply of fresh cigars in the humidor and drinks in the cabinet.

Carl Anderson had refused to have a bedroom made for him downstairs and instead had installed an electric lift. Going up in it herself, she was overcome by the knowledge that for the rest of his life he would have to depend on mechanical means for transport: wheelchairs, lifts, cars. Never again would he be able to use his own legs.

The lift stopped and she went along the corridor to the main bedroom. On her own initiative, though not without a great deal of trepidation, she had asked Mrs Foster to change its decor.

'Mr Anderson will be sleeping in it alone, and it will be better for him if he has something less feminine.'

'What do you have in mind?' Mrs Foster had asked.

'I'll leave it to you.'

Coming into the room today, she knew there was no danger of his being reminded of his erstwhile fiancée. The olive green carpet and the sharp lime and orange curtains were a far cry from the original powder blue and filmy pink silk.

Sensitive to his feelings, Laura did not accompany him from the hospital to Holly Grove, but left him to arrive with Mary—who had agreed to become his private nurse—and his valet. She had toyed with the idea of not seeing him at all that first day, but had decided that too much diplomacy would annoy him and, after giving him a reasonable time to get settled, she went to the house at four o'clock.

The windows glowed with golden light and the warmth of the hall enveloped her as she entered it.

'Mr Anderson is upstairs,' the manservant said. 'He wanted to come down, but Nurse Roberts wouldn't let him.'

'That must have pleased him!'

'He went into one of his quiet tempers.' The valet smiled. He had worked for Carl Anderson for five years and was one of the few people allowed to answer him back. 'He was also expecting *you* to be here when he arrived.'

Without replying to this, Laura ran upstairs. Her employer was not in bed, as she had expected, but sitting in his wheelchair by the window, staring out at the garden and the swimming pool, glimmering faintly in the gathering dusk. He turned his head as Laura came in, but he did not speak, and she went to stand beside his chair. As she did so, the lights around the pool sprang on, turning it into an aquamarine oasis.

'The surgeon said swimming is good for me,' the soft voice spoke behind Laura, but she deliberately remained staring through the window. 'I'm not sure if I didn't make a mistake in coming here to live,' he continued. 'It might have been better if I'd stayed in the flat.'

At this she swung round. 'You did the right thing! This is a beautiful house. You just need to move through the rooms to know it's been happy and well loved. If you——' She stopped, aware of the odd way he was looking at her. 'I'm sorry, Mr Anderson, you must think me very fanciful.'

'Not fanciful, Laura. I just hadn't realised the house meant so much to you.'

Why shouldn't it mean something to me? she wanted to cry. I found it; I decorated it. It's far more my home than Rosemary's. But the habit of years kept her silent and she turned back to the window and stared out with unseeing eyes.

'Don't be embarrassed because you're senti-mental,' he said with mild amusement. 'It's a facet I hadn't expected to find in your character.'

'You only know my office personality.'

'Now you're really putting me in my place!' He put his hand lightly on her arm. 'I've come to know you much more since I've been in hospital. I used to look forward to your visit each day.'

'Because I brought you all the office gossip.'

'It was more than that.' He sighed. 'You're the only person whose head I haven't felt inclined to bite off.'

'If it makes you feel better,' she said whimsically, 'you can bite it any time you like!'

He chuckled and, pressing a button on his wheel-chair, sent it gliding back into the centre of the room. As always it gave her a pang to see him confined in it and, as always, she found it impossible to believe he would never leap from it and walk. How strong and vital he looked! Enforced rest had given him a healthier colour despite the pallor of his skin—and his eyes were fresh and so clear that they looked like summer clouds. Lack of sunshine had darkened his hair to a more subdued beige, but his mouth was as firm, his jawline as determined and his shoulders as broad as they had always been. The turn of his head as he surveyed the room was equally incisive.

'It wasn't like this before,' he muttered.

'Yes, it was.'

'Don't lie to me, Laura.' His voice was as gentle as a snowflake's touch. 'You furnished every single room except the library—to suit Rosemary's taste, and she would never have wanted a bedroom like this.'

'I—er—Mrs Foster didn't feel that powder blue and pink were quite your colours!'

'In that case you should have told her to use black. It would have fitted my mood!'

She refused to rise to this and turned back to the window to draw the curtains.

'Leave them,' he commanded. 'When I wake up in the morning I like to see the sun.' He propelled his chair to the wall and rang the bell. 'Now you're here, maybe I can persuade that damned nurse to let me go downstairs for dinner. She mumbled something about my having it in bed.'

'Mary doesn't mumble,' Laura said drily. 'If I know her, she ordered you to stay in bed.'

'Nobody orders me around in my own home,' he replied. 'The sooner Nurse Roberts realises it the better.'

'She's concerned with your health.'

'So am I. And *I* know what's best for me. My legs may be useless, but my brain still works, and I won't be treated like an imbecile!'

His voice was louder than she had ever heard it. It showed that the control he always kept upon himself was at last beginning to crack. Many times she had wished it would do so, and watching him argue with some of his colleagues, had longed for him to thump the bed or give some other display of temper instead of becoming quieter and more withdrawn.

'Why are you standing there smirking?' he demanded.

'I was smiling, not smirking,' she corrected. 'Your choice of verbs isn't very complimentary.'

'I've never been complimentary to you. Some times I wonder why you stay with me.'

'You pay well,' she said lightly, and watched as he glided towards her. Carl stopped the chair a few feet away and rested his head against the back. The different angle threw his cheekbones into relief and made her realise that though he had regained his spirit, he had not regained the weight he had lost.

'There's something I've been meaning to ask you,' he said quietly. 'After my accident you told me you no longer wished to go abroad. At the time I was delighted to accept your change of mind, but now I don't think I should.'

Laura stared at him, unable to believe he was

61

sending her away. 'D-don't you w-want me to go on working for you?' she stammered.

'Of course I do! But I don't want you sacrificing your life on my account. You said you wanted to travel, and I don't believe you've changed your mind for any reason other than your morbid desire to please me.'

It was a difficult accusation to deny and, even if she did, he was too intelligent to believe her. Yet she had to satisfy him, otherwise he was quite capable of insisting she leave.

'I meant what I said to you that day in the hospital, and I'm not sacrificing myself.'

'Aren't you?'

'No. I genuinely changed my mind. However, I'm willing to promise that if I get another attack of wanderlust, I'll let you know.'

'If I could believe that,' he said slowly, 'I wouldn't feel guilty about letting you stay.'

'I give you my word that I'll never stay with you out of sympathy.' Only from love, her heart cried, but this thought did not show on her face.

'Very well,' he said. 'But I hold you to your promise.'

To Laura's relief, Mary chose that moment to come in. She was not in uniform, having obeyed Carl Anderson's wish not to be reminded of her medical training.

'I enjoy having a pretty woman around,' he had said with some of his old humour, 'but it's bad for my libido if she crackles with starch every time she bends over me.'

Mary now looked at Laura and smiled. 'I suppose Mr Anderson has been complaining because he has to stay in his room tonight?'

'He hasn't said a word about it,' Laura said promptly. 'He's being a model of obedience.'

'How women kid themselves!' he interrupted.

'So do men,' Mary Roberts said, and Laura, looking at him, saw a shadow darken his eyes. Was he finally beginning to realise the sort of person Rosemary was? If only he were, how much happier he would eventually be.

'You'll stay for dinner, won't you, Laura?' he questioned.

'If you wish.'

His head tilted. 'Always at my service, Laura. I don't know what I would do without you.'

CHAPTER SIX

WITHIN a few weeks Laura settled down into a routine far different from the one she had previously had. Each morning she went to the office, collected her employer's mail and took it to Holly Grove where she spent the morning taking dictation and getting the various calls around the world which the correspondence frequently necessitated.

At noon Carl took an hour off for his physiotherapy, and though to begin with she counted this time as her lunch hour, he soon asked her to have lunch with him instead. At two o'clock he sent his wheelchair gliding up the ramp fixed to the back of the new shooting brake he had bought himself. He had brusquely refused to be carried into the back of his Rolls-Royce, saying he felt more of a man if he could do things for himself instead of being shifted around like a parcel. He seemed oblivious of the curious stares from passers-by as he and Laura drove down to the office, and if any of them showed more than average curiosity by peering in, he would cheerfully wave to them, which sent them scuttling off in embarrassment.

He remained at the office for the rest of the day and it was here that most of the people came to see him. Laura knew he found it frustrating to have all the information he required come to him second-hand. He was a man who had always done things for himself, yet now he was having to depend on others.

His decision to change this particular aspect of his life came without warning, reminding her—lest she had forgotten—that he was not a man one could ever profess to know completely. It happened on a bitterly cold December afternoon when, instead of the chauffeur taking them from the house to the office, Carl ordered the man to go to the Lambeth building site.

Laura caught her breath at his casual tone. No one would ever guess he was going to the site where he had had the accident which had ruined his life.

'The work hasn't fallen behind schedule,' she said quickly. 'Mr Durban was there yesterday. There's no reason for you to go.'

He did not answer, but the look he slanted in her direction made her lapse into silence. They both remained quiet for the rest of the journey, though when the car reached the Lambeth site she saw the fine film of sweat on his forehead. He slid his chair down the ramp, then waited for the foreman—whom he had obviously warned ahead of time—to come forward and propel his chair along the uneven ground.

'Come with me, Laura,' he called impatiently. 'I want you to take some notes.'

For the next hour he was trundled from one part of the site to the other. To begin with many of the workmen stopped and watched him, but he appeared oblivious of their interest, though the shine on his forehead did not disappear and a flush developed on his cheekbones.

It was Laura who finally insisted they return to the office by pretending to feel terribly cold, though as they went up in the lift and she undid her coat, he chided her for being a poor liar.

'You don't look cold at all. Your cheeks are glowing like a robin redbreast.'

'My feet are frozen,' she asserted.

'You're a bit like a robin in other ways too,' he continued, giving her an appraising look. 'It's that brown hair of yours and those warm brown eyes.'

'Robins aren't brown.'

'In my imagination they are.' He half smiled. 'There's something cheery and comforting about a robin.' He gave her another longer look. 'On second thoughts you aren't like a bird. You're far too calm and you move much more gracefully. I remember my mother once reading me a story about a robin redbreast. Perhaps that's why the simile came to mind.' The lift doors opened and he glided out. 'You have the same colouring as my mother. I never noticed it before.'

'You rarely talk about her,' she said.

'I think of her a great deal, though,' he said abruptly. 'Particularly since my accident.'

It was from Mary Roberts that Laura first heard her employer was having a series of tests at a leading neurological hospital. He had merely told her he would not be free to see anyone for two days and had led her to believe he was having additional physiotherapy which might help him to move around on crutches in the foreseeable future. It was a shock to learn this was untrue and that the exercises were, in fact, intensive physical tests to try and discover why he was suddenly having acute pain in his legs.

Laura had grown so used to seeing him in a wheelchair that even when she dreamed about him—as she frequently did—it was always to see him in this position, and she had taken it for granted that because he could not use his legs, he had no feeling in them.

'He must be having intense pain if he's willing to take tests to find out what's causing it,' she said.

'I took it for granted you knew. Otherwise I wouldn't have mentioned it.' Mary looked perturbed. 'He usually tells you everything.'

'Only concerning his work. He never discusses his personal affairs.'

'Does he ever talk about the steel butterfly?'

'*Who?*'

'His ex-fiancée. That's the way I think of her. She looks fragile, yet she's as tough as steel.'

'We never talk about her,' Laura said shortly. 'But I'm sure he's still in love with her. If he could walk again ...'

'That's what I was afraid of.'

Laura frowned, quick to see where Mary's thoughts had taken her. 'Could the pain in his legs mean he might be getting some movement back in them?'

'That's the obvious conclusion.'

'How many more tests must he have before he knows?'

'He should be getting the results any time.'

Laura knew better than to ask Mary to let her know what they were, for the girl was already upset at having talked about her patient. 'I won't let Mr Anderson know you've told me anything about the tests,' she repeated reassuringly. 'When he has the results I'm sure he'll be delighted to tell me himself.'

How tragically wrong she was she learned when

she came to the house on Monday morning and found him still in bed. Normally he was in his wheelchair by the time she arrived, but today the chair stood empty by the window and he lay in bed propped up by pillows. His skin was flushed and on first coming in she thought how remarkably well he looked, but moving forward she saw the greyness about his mouth and the bleakness in his eyes. Her training kept her face devoid of expression and she drew up a chair and sat beside him, notebook in her lap.

'You should soon be getting a telephone call from Tokyo, Mr Anderson. It came to the office a little while ago and the switchboard gave them this number.'

'I'm not taking any calls.'

'It's Mr Tanako.' She named one of the biggest industrialists in Japan.

'I don't care if it's the Dalai Lama!' he said. 'I am not taking any calls.'

'If you don't feel well enough to work, I can come back later.' She stood up to go, but his outstretched hand bade her remain.

'I'm all right, Laura—for the next two years.'

Not sure what he was trying to say, she waited.

'I don't know if Mary told you that I've been having tests at the hospital?' Laura tried to look noncommittal. 'Mr Edwards came to see me on Saturday morning with the result.' His hands moved closer together, almost as if he wished to clasp them, then they remained still and apart. 'At the most, he gives me two years to live.'

Laura went on looking at him, hoping that if she did he would grin and tell her he was joking; that the surgeon had said exactly the opposite and that in two years' time he would be walking properly. But the silver grey eyes remained lifeless, giving her the feeling that she was looking at a statue.

'Is he sure?' she asked in cool, precise tones.

'He'd hardly be likely to tell me such a thing if he wasn't.' The voice was cool and precise as her own. 'At most I have two years. It may even be less.'

'But why? What has happened?'

'Apparently I have some degenerative condition caused by spinal pressure. I won't bore you with the details. What it means is that I'll gradually start to lose the use of my muscles. And once the heart is affected . . .'

'I don't believe it,' Laura said. 'All you have is one man's opinion. You must call in someone else. Go to America, Switzerland——'

'Edwards is one of the top men in his field.' For the first time the bleakness in his eyes diminished. 'I know you can't believe it, Laura. That's how I felt on Saturday when I first heard, but I've had time to come to terms with it.'

'You can't come to terms with dying!'

'We're all dying from the moment we're born—if you'll forgive the truism. I'm in the unfortunate—or perhaps fortunate—position of knowing exactly when it will be for me!'

'Fortunate!' Blindly she went to the window. 'Is it because of Rosemary that you don't want to live? Because you can't get that little bitch out of your mind?' Her discretion had gone to the wind, but she did not care. The man she loved was dying. He was even glad of it—and all because he could not face life without a girl who was not worthy to clean his shoes.

The man in the bed made no reply, and as the silence lengthened, Laura's anger was overtaken by shame. 'I'm sorry, Mr Anderson. I know you told me not to mention Miss Carlton's name, but . . .'

'Forget it. I realise that what I told you has come as a shock, but when I used the word "fortunate" I wasn't thinking of Rosemary. I meant knowing you're going to die gives you a chance to put your affairs in order. I have a big and successful company and no family to whom I can leave it. I also have a house and a lot of property. It will take me time to decide what to do with it all.'

'Forget it and concentrate on living,' she said fiercely. 'I won't let you give up hope. Each day scientists discover something new. You must see other doctors—go all over the world if necessary.'

'I'm not writing myself off yet,' he said whimsically, 'but it's foolish to live on false hope. Sit down and stop looking so tragic.'

She did as he ordered, but for the life of her could not summon up a smile. Her eyes were burning, but they were tearless, and she managed to give the impression of being in control of herself. By dint of great effort she took down the notes he dictated, and it was only as she went to leave the room at noon—when he normally had his physiotherapy—that she referred to the news he had told her earlier.

'Sit down again, Laura. I'm not going to have any more massage or exercise. There's no point putting myself through the agony of it.' He paused, then said: 'Apart from Mr Edwards and Mary, you're the only other person to know. My lawyer will have to be told, of course, but no one else. I don't want people's sympathy.'

Huskily she promised to do as he asked.

'You didn't need to make that promise,' he replied. 'You are the most discreet woman I know.'

'All the virtues and no vices,' she said, trying to bring some lightness into the conversation.

'I'd better put it in writing,' he teased, and then lost his humour as he saw into the future. 'I would like to feel that when you stop working for *me*, you won't need to work for anyone else. I hope you won't object if I make arrangements to that effect?'

Her face flamed, and though she knew he was trying to be kind it was a gesture which she found intolerable. 'I'd hate to be a lady of leisure, Mr Anderson. I want nothing from you.'

Nothing except your love, she said silently, and wished she had the courage to tell him so. Yet if he knew she loved him he would be too embarrassed to go on seeing her. Wryly she wondered if he realised how much he had come to depend on her since his accident. She had even taken to coming here on a Saturday and Sunday morning, and had only refrained from doing so this weekend because he had told Mary to ring up on Saturday to say he was tired and wanted to rest. Instead of which he had seen the surgeon and then gone through his own private hell without anyone to comfort him.

'You're a nice girl, Laura,' he said gently. 'You should have a husband and children to take care of, not be bothering yourself with my affairs.'

'Not all women want a husband and children,' she replied.

'I refuse to believe *you* don't.' His look was keen. 'I'm not the most sensitive of men when it comes

71

to understanding the way a woman's mind works, but I would lay odds that you are the type to want a husband and a brood of children to dote upon.'

'We still have some letters to deal with, Mr Anderson.'

'I can take a hint,' he replied. 'That insensitive I am not!'

In the days that followed, he did not alter his routine and Laura found it hard to credit that he knew his days were numbered. He dealt with projects that were being planned for three years ahead, when he knew he would not be around to see them, and he made decisions that would affect everyone long after he was dead. It was as if he were trying to ensure that the company ran the way he wanted it to even when he was no longer there to see it. He was filled with new energy and started going to other people's offices in the building, instead of having them come to see him, so that she grew used to watching his wheelchair zoom past her desk on its way down the corridor. Because of this it was all the more of a shock to enter her office one morning and have Miss Jackson slap a tabloid down in front of her.

'Isn't it terrible about Mr Anderson?' the girl gulped. 'I can't believe it.'

'Believe what?' Laura asked.

'That he's dying. It says so here.' Miss Jackson opened the paper and pointed to a photograph of her employer. 'It's all there,' she whispered. 'About his accident and his engagement being broken, and now the news that he only has two years to live.'

Laura snatched up the paper and skimmed through the article. It was an appalling infringement upon a person's private life and she shook with anger. 'Has this story appeared in any other paper?'

'Not as far as I know. But it has such a huge circulation, everyone is bound to read it. Is it true?'

'Don't be ridiculous!' Laura snapped.

'But they say he has only two years to live.'

'Newspapers will say anything to make a lurid story. Now dump that paper in the wastepaper basket and forget it.'

Though she could tell Miss Jackson to forget the article, she could not command the rest of the staff, and soon the whole office was buzzing with it. She was not surprised when Mr Rogers rang through and asked her to come and see him.

'What's all this news about Mr Anderson?' he asked without preamble.

'I suggest you ask Mr Anderson,' she replied composedly.

'I'm asking *you*. Is it true or isn't it?' As she remained silent, his small eyes glinted. 'Don't get above yourself, Miss Pearson, it doesn't become you.'

'It's better than snooping!' she retorted, beyond caring what she said. This man meant nothing to her and she was not going to be intimidated by him.

'Just because you're Mr Anderson's secretary, you think you can get away with everything,' he said unpleasantly. 'But if this article is true, you'd better start looking to your future. Or has Mr Anderson taken care of it for you?'

With a gasp she ran out, but once in the corridor she stopped and leaned against the wall, her body shaking too much for her to move. She was still standing there when a wheelchair glided to a stop beside her and with an enormous effort she stood up straight.

'Mr—Mr Anderson,' she stammered. 'I was j-just coming up to the house. You don't normally come in during the morning.'

'Mary showed me the newspaper,' he said grimly. 'I thought the best way of scotching the article was to come in early, carrying a copy of it!'

Only then did she give him her full attention. He was wearing dark blue slacks and a fine wool sweater of the same colour. It fitted him snugly and the muscles of his chest were clearly visible. He looked young and strong and it was hard to credit he could not rise from his chair and stride out boldly. Stricken by the knowledge, she stared into his face. He was smiling faintly, though it did not reach his eyes, and she knew what an effort he was making to appear unconcerned. It made her own anger against Mr Rogers seem a petty thing. Why should she worry what anyone thought of her, when all she cared about was the man beside her?

'Why were you coming out of Mr Rogers' office?' he asked.

'He wanted to see me.'

'What did he say to upset you?'

'Nothing.'

'Don't lie to me, Laura. You were leaning against the wall as if you were going to faint.'

'That has nothing to do with Mr Rogers,' she said quickly. 'It was because of Miss Jackson. She gave me a copy of the article when I arrived.'

'Is that what Rogers wanted to see you obout?'

She nodded. 'Let's go into your office.'

'You go to the office,' he said evenly. 'I'm going to talk to Bob.' He leaned forward, opened the director's door and glided in without a glance backwards. 'Good morning,' she heard him say cheerily. 'Have you read this rubbish about me in the paper?'

Not waiting to hear any more, Laura fled.

CHAPTER SEVEN

THE article in the tabloid was not picked up by any other daily paper that week, but on Sunday, the tabloid's sister paper published a further article. It went into great detail about Carl Anderson's illness. There was a lot of medical jargon used and Laura, reading it, knew it would not be as easy to disprove this story as the previous one.

On Monday the Anderson shares dropped on the stock market and Carl Anderson slapped an injunction on to the editor's desk forbidding him to make any further reference to the company, and stating that he would sue anyone who wrote about his private life or health.

'One has little enough privacy as it is,' he told Laura grimly, 'without newspapers being allowed to run amok. They can make one's life intolerable.'

Laura nodded, forbearing to say she already found life intolerable. She had been sure that given time she would be able to face the prospect of his death with equanimity. But the more she tried to be rational about it the less rational she became. It was impossible for her to accept the fact that he was going to die within two years. Yet she dared not talk about it with him. She was there to keep him cheerful, not to distress him with her own morbid thoughts. It was only to Mary that she could show her despair, and though the nurse sympathised, she was unable to give her any comfort.

'I've spoken to Mr Edwards myself,' she told Laura, 'but he told me exactly what Mr Anderson told you.'

They were sitting in an Italian restaurant in Soho, for they had taken to meeting out once a week for dinner. Carl Anderson knew about it and always insisted that Mary use his car and chauffeur.

'I suppose you know he's heard from the steel butterfly?' the nurse continued as she replenished her coffee cup.

Laura set her own cup sharply on to its saucer. 'No, I didn't. When was this?'

'A couple of days after that article in the Sunday paper. I was in his bedroom when the phone rang and I answered it. Unfortunately my conscience wouldn't let me hang around and listen to what they were saying, but from the few words I heard, I gathered the South African papers had picked up the news and she was ringing to see if it was true.'

'You would think she'd have the decency to leave him alone!' Laura exclaimed. 'The last thing in the world he wants is sympathy.'

'She might be willing to offer him her love.'

Laura gaped at Mary, who gave her a pitying smile in return.

'Honestly, Laura, didn't it enter your head that this is exactly what Rosemary would do if she learned that Mr Anderson was dying?'

'But why? She can't bear illness.'

'She can't bear being tied for life to a cripple,' Mary corrected, 'but it would be different to be tied to him for a couple of years. After all, think what she'd stand to gain.'

'One telephone call isn't all that much to go on,' Laura said slowly.

'He's had two more since then. Care to take a bet that the next thing she'll do is to come back and declare her undying love?'

'No bets,' Laura sighed. 'I have a feeling you may be right.'

On Sunday morning, two days after they had dined together, Mary telephoned Laura to say that what they had both feared had come true. 'She's with him now,' Mary concluded. 'Arrived in a taxi with five suitcases. My bet is that she's here to stay.'

Laura was desperately anxious to know how Carl Anderson had reacted, but she could not bring herself to ask. Instead she said casually: 'I'll let you know if I agree with you when I see her tomorrow.'

'Aren't you coming over today?'

'I don't fancy being a third wheel,' Laura said with an effort at humour.

'Has he telephoned and asked you not to come?'

'No.'

'Then don't stay away. If you do, he'll guess that I rang and told you Rosemary is here.'

It was only because of this that Laura went to Holly Grove later in the morning. Both she and Carl Anderson had long since given up pretending there were any business reasons for her to see him on a Saturday and Sunday, and though he occasionally grumbled at her for wasting her weekends on him, he was always disappointed when she prepared to go home, and frequently asked her to stay for the evening. But today she knew it would be different and, as she rang the front door bell, she was in two minds whether or not to depart without seeing him.

'Mr Anderson is in the drawing room,' the Spanish butler said as he took her coat.

'Is Miss Carlton with him?'

José nodded and again Laura wished she had not come. But it was too late to do anything about it and bracing herself for the meeting, she knocked on the drawing room door and went in.

Carl was in his wheelchair by the fireplace. Despite the central heating a log fire burned in the grate and, on a hassock in front of it, Rosemary perched gracefully, her soft wool skirts spread around her, her long fair hair combed away from her face in a style that was at once appealing and disarmingly young. She rose at Laura's entrance and came forward to greet her affectionately.

'It's wonderful for me to find Carl settled in this beautiful house,' she said.

Laura sought for the right reply, but could not find it. She glanced at her employer and saw he was watching them both. There was a cynical twist on his mouth that she had not seen before, but she refused to read too much into it. *She* might see the real reason for Rosemary's return, but that did not mean Carl Anderson did.

'Come to the fire and get warm, Laura,' he said. 'You look frozen.'

'I had to wait ages for a bus.'

'Don't expect my sympathy. I keep telling you to use the car and chauffeur.' He glanced at Rosemary. 'I still can't make Laura accept the little luxuries of life.'

'I wouldn't call a chauffeur-driven Rolls a *little* luxury,' Laura smiled.

'You'll soon accept it as normal,' he said.

In the act of stretching her hands to the fire, Laura glanced at him. But she could not read his expression, for he had turned to speak to Rosemary.

'It was foolish of you to fly over without warning me. I told you it would be a wasted journey.'

'I didn't believe you,' Rosemary replied. 'I know how proud you are and I didn't expect you to say you missed me or wanted me to come back.'

Laura retreated from the fire, her body hot, but not from the flames. 'I think I'll go,' she said quickly.

'Don't be ridiculous,' Carl Anderson said loudly. 'We can't keep it a secret for ever.'

'What secret?' Rosemary asked.

'That Laura has agreed to become my wife.'

There was an electric silence; Rosemary's face blanched and she was too astounded to notice that Laura's had done exactly the same. 'You are—you are going to marry your secretary?'

'I am going to marry Laura,' he replied evenly. 'I should have told you when you first arrived, but you were tired from your flight and I wanted to give you time to recover.'

Rosemary shook her head, her expression still bemused. 'Is this some sort of a joke?'

'It's hardly a joking matter.' Dexterously he swivelled his chair round to Laura's side and, before she could escape his hold, reached out and caught her hand. His grip was tight, warning her to be silent. 'We would have announced it a couple of weeks ago if it hadn't been for that nonsense printed in the paper about me,' he continued. 'But after that bit of notoriety I felt I'd had enough publicity to last me a lifetime.' He raised Laura's hand to his cheek. 'We're planning to slip away one morning and get married quietly.'

'No!' Rosemary gasped. 'You don't mean it. You love me, Carl, you know you do.'

'I did,' he said, and his grip on Laura's hand tightened so fiercely that she winced. Instantly the grip eased, though he did not release her hand. 'I never thought I would be saying this to you, Rosemary, but I stopped loving you a long time ago.'

'It's only four months since I left you,' she cried. 'I wouldn't call that long.'

'When you spend your life in a wheelchair,' he said heavily, 'a day can seem like a year. That's how it was with me until I fell in love with Laura.'

'You don't love her,' Rosemary exclaimed. 'You feel gratitude! For heaven's sake, Carl, you knew her years before you knew me. If you were going to fall in love with her, you'd have done so ages ago.'

'I probably needed an accident to bring me to my senses.'

He continued to speak, but Laura was unable to take in anything he said. Yet he must have sounded plausible, for she was aware of Rosemary sinking on to a chair and huddling forward, like a child in pain.

'I won't believe it until you're married,' she whispered. 'I won't! I won't!'

'Then you'd better stay and come to the wedding,' Carl said quietly.

Rosemary stared at him, her blue eyes filling with tears. She looked so hurt and broken that Laura would not have blamed him if he had lunged forward and pulled her into his arms. Instead he moved restlessly and the blanket covering his legs twitched.

'You may stay here as my guest, Rosemary, but if you do, Laura will have to stay here with you.'

'You must be crazy if you think I'll do that!' Rosemary leaned forward and fell on her knees beside the wheelchair. 'I love you, Carl. You can't marry anyone else. I want to spend my life with you.'

'Two years isn't much of a lifetime.'

Rosemary's head jerked upwards. Her expression froze and the tears glittered on her lashes like ice drops. 'So it *is* true,' she gasped. 'When I asked you this morning, why did you deny it?'

'I was waiting for Laura,' he replied, and once again drew her hand to his cheek and then to his lips.

It was this last gesture which convinced Rosemary he meant what he said, and with a cry of pain she sprang to her feet and ran from the room.

As the door slammed behind her, Laura pulled her hand free and put the distance of the room between herself and the wheelchair. She was filled with an anger far deeper than any she had ever experienced, and she fought to control it. With all her heart she had wanted Carl to fight Rosemary, but she had never dreamed he would use herself as the weapon. For that was all she was: his weapon of defence against the beautiful girl he still loved.

'It wasn't kind of you to use me,' she said icily.

'I didn't intend to. It just happened. When you walked into the room and looked at me, it suddenly struck me as a marvellous idea.'

'A marvellous get-out,' she corrected.

There was the soft sound of wheels on carpet and she knew he had come behind her, but she would not turn and look at him.

'Don't be angry with me, Laura. Try and understand why I did it.'

'I *am* trying. But it doesn't make sense. Or do you expect me to believe you don't love Miss Carlton any longer?'

'Of course I love her!'

'Then why the pretence?' She swung round and faced him. 'If you still love her, why——?'

'Because I don't want to marry her,' he interrupted. 'Listen to me, Laura. Do you think I believe that Rosemary came back because she had second thoughts about tying herself to a cripple? She came here because she knows my time is limited. She's prepared to sacrifice herself for two years, to hide the repugnance she'd feel if I touched her, if I held her close to my body, because she knows that in a short space of time she'd be a widow of undreamed-of wealth!'

'Don't talk like that!' Laura cried.

'It's true! You've always known the sort of girl Rosemary is.' His eyes glittered silver in a grey-tinged face. 'She gave herself away a hundred times, but I was too blind to see it. Even when it came to this house, she didn't love me enough to want to furnish it herself. She never saw it as our home— only as a background in which she could scintillate.' His hands clenched and he banged one fist against the other. 'In a way I should be grateful I had the accident. If I hadn't, I would have married her and ... God!' He lowered his head. 'At least I'd have had *some* happiness with her! This way I've had none.'

Jealousy drowned Laura's sympathy and she looked at him with something akin to dislike. 'I'm sure you can still have some happiness with her,' she said coldly, 'providing you're willing to marry her.'

'And what do you suggest I do with my mind? Blank it out? Do you think I could make love to her without knowing the revulsion she feels? No, Laura, I've done the only thing possible.'

'For today,' she said evenly. 'But what about to-morrow and the day after?'

'What do you mean?'

'I mean that she'll be back. The stakes are far too high for her to give up so easily. She'll stay in London and after a few days she'll come and see you again. It won't take her long to realise that your engagement to me is a lie.'

'Need it be?'

She stared at him uncomprehendingly and he moved his chair closer.

'Need it be a lie, Laura? Why can't it be true? You aren't in love with anyone else, are you?'

'No, but——'

'Then why shouldn't we get married? I wouldn't expect it to be a real marriage,' he said hastily.

With a murmur she turned her back on him. In moments of foolish day-dreaming she had often wondered what it would be like if Carl Anderson asked her to be his wife. But now that he had done it, she wished with all her heart that he hadn't.

'You're dramatising the situation, Mr Anderson. It would be ludicrous for us to get married just be-cause you don't want to marry Miss Carlton.'

'Why is it ludicrous? If you turn me down, I mightn't be able to hold out against her. I'm only half a man,' he said huskily, 'but I'm a man for all that. When she's near me, I . . . Please,' he pleaded, 'don't let me make a fool of myself with her. All I have left is my pride. Help me to keep it.'

'I—I——' She struggled to find the right words, but since she did not know what to say, no words came.

'It wouldn't be for long,' he said quietly. 'Only two years.'

'Don't!' she choked and, swinging round, held out her hands to him. 'Very well,' she whispered. 'If you're quite sure.'

'Perfectly sure. And thank you, Laura. I knew that you—of all women—wouldn't let me down.'

Neither of them spoke after this, and the only sound in the room was the crackle of the logs.

CHAPTER EIGHT

LAURA became Mrs Carl Anderson two days before Christmas, with Mary and the valet Max as the only witnesses. To avoid publicity they returned straight to the house where she was surprised to find that Carl—how strange it was to call him by his first name—had arranged a champagne luncheon.

'We're neither of us going to pretend this is a love match,' he had said the night before, 'but I want you to believe me when I say you're the only woman I totally admire and trust.'

Laura remembered this as he raised his glass and toasted her, and wondered what he would say if he knew how much she loved him. After lunch Mary and Max left them alone and they sat on either side of the fireplace in the drawing room. She was wearing a red dress, a colour she had never worn before, and she felt him staring at her appraisingly.

'You should wear red more often,' he commented finally. 'It suits you.'

'Red for robin redbreast,' she reminded him.

'Talking of red reminds me of something.' He reached into his pocket and took out a little box which he tossed into her lap.

She opened it and saw a large, dark ruby glowing up at her.

'If it doesn't fit,' he murmured, 'you can easily get it altered.' Still she went on looking at it and he moved his chair over to her. 'Put it on and let me see what it looks like.'

With a reluctance she could not understand she went to put it on her right hand, but he gently took it away from her and put it on her engagement finger, now marked by a circle of platinum.

'It's your engagement ring,' he explained.

She was moved and tried to hide it. 'I didn't need one.'

'I'm going to give you lots of things you don't need,' he replied. 'You are my wife and I want you to have everything money can buy.'

She held out her hand and looked at the ruby. 'This is beautiful, Carl, and I appreciate you buying it for me, but please don't buy me anything else. I married you because ...' She stopped, then said firmly: 'I don't want anything from you.'

'I know you don't. That's why I want you to have everything.' He leaned forward, his eyes searching her face. 'It will all come to you when I die: the house, the company I built up, everything.'

'No!' She jumped to her feet. His chair was so near that she stumbled on it and was only saved from falling by his arms coming round her waist. He kept them there, then deliberately pulled her down on to his lap.

'Let me give you what I can,' he said softly. 'There's so much that I can't.' One hand came up to the back of her head and drew it forward until his mouth could rest on hers. For a second it remained there motionless, then the pressure increased and he pulled her closer.

Laura clung to him, uncaring that she was giving herself away, knowing only that at last she was where she belonged, where she had always wanted to be. It did not matter that he loved another woman. This was as close to heaven as she was likely to get and she did not have the strength to turn away from it.

'Carl,' she whispered, and caressed his silver fair hair. It was like silk to the touch and she ran her fingers through it and down the side of his cheek. His lips moved gently upon hers and then placed feather-light kisses on her closed eyelids.

'Dear Laura, how sweet you are.'

It was the words 'dear Laura' that brought her back to her senses. Dear, sensible Laura. The ever-helpful, always available secretary. The girl he had married in order to escape from the woman he loved. Dear Laura, who he would never want to be his darling.

Carefully she pushed him away and eased herself up from his lap. She knew he was watching her and she made a pretence of smoothing her skirt.

'You aren't angry with me, are you?' he asked.

'For kissing me?' She marvelled that she could keep her voice cool. 'This is an emotional moment for both of us. Even a—a marriage like ours takes a bit of getting used to. Why shouldn't you kiss me? After all, we're friends—even though I *am* your wife!'

He smiled, at ease again. 'You're a surprising girl, Laura. There are depths to you that I hadn't realised.'

'Unfathomable depths,' she replied. 'Beware of them.'

'I have nothing to be wary of with you. That's why I married you, remember?'

'How can I forget it!' She turned to the fire and

put on a log it did not need. 'What are we going to do for Christmas?'

'I haven't given it a thought. What would you like to do?'

'Have a quiet stay-at-home holiday.' She looked round the room. 'This will be the first night I've spent here, yet I feel as if it's my home.'

'It's yours more than it was ever Rosemary's.' His voice was bleak and he propelled his chair to the bureau by the window, where he made a pretence of looking through some magazines.

Laura watched him, knowing that the months ahead would not be easy for either of them. Today Carl looked on her with affection and gratitude, but there would be many times when he would look at her and wish she were Rosemary; and those were the times when he would hate her and himself too.

'Carl,' she said abruptly. 'There's something I want to say.'

He swivelled round. 'Not a divorce yet!'

She smiled. 'Not yet. But I ... if I do anything that gets on your nerves ... if you ever want me to move out ... you just have to say so.'

'Thank you,' he said gravely, 'but I don't foresee the likelihood. I'm much more likely to get on *your* nerves!'

'Oh no,' she exclaimed, 'I've been your secretary for too long.' Embarrassed, she put her hand to her mouth. 'Oh, lord, that wasn't a diplomatic thing to say!'

He grinned, his bleakness gone. 'Thank goodness you can be indiscreet. I'd hate to have a perfect wife!'

Yet in the weeks ahead that was exactly what

Laura tried to be. Living at Holly Grove she saw a different side to Carl. As his private secretary she had come to know him well, but she was surprised at the greater intimacy that grew between them now that she was actually sharing his home. Since the first night of their marriage there had been no further emotional display from him, yet they were so mentally attuned that Laura was frequently aware of his thoughts before he even expressed them. Many times she longed to be physically close to him, and it was then that she envisaged the future and was haunted by it. If he had to die young, at least let his death be a quick one and not a lingering diminishing of strength that would leave him feeble and totally dependent on others.

She tried not to dwell on these thoughts and, during the day, she was successful in keeping them at bay; but at night she paced her bedroom and found it impossible to envisage this house without its owner and her life without him at its centre. Never by word or gesture did Carl give indication that he worried about the limited time left to him, and it was not until they had been married for two months that he spoke to her about the plans he was making for the future.

'I wish you would get another medical opinion!' she burst out. 'I don't know how you can listen to Mr Edwards without——'

'It wasn't only Mr Edwards,' Carl interrupted. 'He called in other specialists too.'

'I'm sure there are more you could see.'

'Hundreds,' he agreed. 'But that doesn't mean any of them can help me. One can only go to the best person available, and I assure you Mr Edwards has a worldwide reputation. Now stop being dramatic and listen to the plans I've made for the company.'

'I don't care about the company!' she cried.

'It's going to be yours.'

'No!' She jumped to her feet. 'No, Carl. When I married you I told you I didn't want anything from you, and I still mean it.'

'I know you do. But I want you to have it. You're my wife.'

'Only because you needed someone to protect you from Rosemary.'

It was the first time she had mentioned Rosemary since their marriage, though many times her presence had hovered between them like an evil spirit. But one could not continue to pretend Rosemary did not exist.

'Whatever my reasons for marrying you,' Carl said, 'you are now my wife and I have every intention of providing for you.'

'If you leave me any money I'll give it away,' she said vehemently. 'I'm not a child, and I won't be treated as one.'

'Won't you take *anything* from me?'

'No.' She flung out her hand as she spoke and the ruby on her finger glowed like a flame. 'I'll keep the ring and the—and the clothes I have, but nothing more.'

'Even if I told you that by refusing to let me take care of you, you'll make me extremely unhappy?'

'That's an unfair way of putting it,' she protested.

'It's the way I feel. You married me to protect me from my own weakness, so at least let me show you some of my strength. If I can provide for your future I will at least feel like a man.'

91

'Money has nothing to do with strength of character. You don't need to repay me for what I did. I married you because——' She fell silent, knowing he would find in it only what he was capable of understanding and, since he regarded her as his friend, the secret of her love for him was safe.

'I'm not offering you charity,' he said slowly. 'If you won't accept my fortune, at least let me take decent care of you.'

She gazed at him, astonished that he could look at her without knowing how deeply she loved him. How handsome he was with his thick hair and strong features; his clear grey eyes and mobile mouth. It was indecent for them to be discussing what would happen to her own life when his no longer existed. Because she knew that to argue with him would only prolong the discussion, she shook her head.

'I won't stop you from doing what you think is right, Carl, but promise not to—not to leave me a lot of money. There are so many other things you can do with it.'

'I'll talk to Duncan about that.'

'Duncan?' she questioned.

'Duncan Thorpe—my lawyer.'

She nodded. Several times she had heard him mention the name Thorpe & Mulvaney, but this was the first occasion he had spoken of his lawyer by name.

'I think it's a good idea for you to talk it over with Mr Thorpe,' she said. 'If he's unbiased, I'm sure he'll agree with what I've suggested.'

'Duncan is always unbiased,' Carl informed her. 'In that way he's like me.'

'You're the most biased person I know!' He gave

her such a look of injured innocence that she laughed outright. 'You're terribly biased, Carl. You're as full of prejudice as a colander is of holes!'

'I can never accuse you of using flattery to entice me.'

'I've never tried to entice you.' The instant she spoke she regretted it, for he gave her a long look, one pale eyebrow raised.

'You aren't obvious with your charms, Laura, but many women, far less pretty than you, get themselves more attention.'

'I don't want that kind of attention. I want to be seen as a person, not as some sexual object.'

'Do I hear the strident plea of female emancipation?' he smiled.

'We all carry our freedom within us. One can't lay down hard and fast rules for everyone.'

'Society can't live without rules, Laura. One has to protect the weak. And for centuries women have been weak and subservient to men because of their physical differences. The burden of childbirth and taking care of their offspring have been their most debilitating factors.'

'Liberation won't lessen those,' Laura retorted. 'Most women will always find it a wrench to choose between their career and being with their children. It isn't just men's outlook towards women that will have to change—it's the entire role that men and women play in society.' Unwilling to become too serious, she gave a deprecating laugh. 'It's far too big a subject for us to talk about.'

'It would also take too much of our time,' he said sombrely. 'And time is the one thing I don't have.'

His hands clenched in a convulsive movement

that gave away more than he realised. Laura's bones seemed to melt with tenderness for him. The urge to comfort him was so great that she could not stop herself and, bending down to his chair, she cradled his head in her arms.

'Oh, Carl,' she whispered brokenly, 'if only there was something I could do!'

'You're here with me,' he said indistinctly. 'That's all I need.'

Three days after this incident, Carl told Laura he had invited Duncan Thorpe to lunch and, assuming it to be a business one, she said she would go into town and do some shopping.

'That's what I like to hear,' he commented. 'Buy yourself lots of pretty things. I dislike seeing you in the same clothes all the time.'

'I don't wear the same clothes,' she protested.

'They seem that way to me.'

He was blunt and truthful, the way she had always known him to be, and her hurt was overtaken by amusement, particularly when he said: 'Stop being a robin redbreast and become a peacock.'

'A peahen,' she corrected. 'And they're very drab creatures!'

'Don't confuse me with scientific facts,' he grinned. 'A peacock I said and a peacock I mean! Go out and do all the extravagant things I can't do *for* you.'

Knowing that if he had been able to do them she would not be married to him, she felt her light-heartedness evaporate. But she was careful not to let him know and promised to dazzle him with a wardrobe in the primary colours.

'Don't come back late,' he warned. 'I want to

introduce Duncan to you.'

'Will he still be here, then?'

'I expect so. We have a lot to talk over. The only reason you haven't seen him before is that he's been in New York for the last year. They have an American office and he went over to ginger it up.'

Deciding Duncan Thorpe could not be the old family lawyer she had envisaged, she looked forward to meeting him and, returning to the house later that afternoon, after a shopping spree which she hoped would satisfy Carl, she went into the study to take tea with the two men.

'On time as always,' Carl said and, holding out his hand to her, looked at the man who had risen from the settee. 'Duncan, I would like to introduce you to my wife.'

It was the first time Carl had called her his wife. Normally when he referred to her, he did so by her name. Laura held out her hand and felt it taken by a thin, hard-boned one, then looked up into deep-set eyes almost as pale a grey as Carl's. In every other respect Duncan Thorpe was different. At five feet nine he was several inches shorter than his client and was slim to the point of thinness. But the grip of his hand showed her he was all muscle and the fluid way he moved indicated that he did not rely for exercise solely on shifting a gearstick.

'We meet at last, Mrs Anderson. I've heard a great deal about you.'

She smiled and moved across to the tea trolley which José was wheeling forward. The lawyer was younger even than she had anticipated, and she found it difficult to imagine Carl taking advice from someone who was probably his own age.

Sipping her tea and eating a scone while the two

men talked, she had a better chance of judging their relationship. They were on Christian name terms and were obviously close friends, which was another fact she had not expected, for she had always considered Carl too busy to devote time to people—other than the women he had always found so necessary to him. Her hands trembled and she set her cup down. She was the only woman in his life now, and after her, there would be no one.

'Carl tells me you used to work for him.' Duncan Thorpe was looking in her direction. 'I can see why he never let us have any of our meetings in his office. He was obviously keeping you hidden!'

Laura glanced at Carl and, as if he knew what she was thinking, his eyes crinkled with wry amusement.

'Quit the act, Duncan,' he said. 'Laura knows you're the only intimate friend I have and she wouldn't expect me to lie to you about the reason for our marriage. She became my wife to save me from an even nastier fate, and in current terms, we're only platonic friends!'

Laura reddened and wished Carl had not been so blunt, but she understood when he continued:

'That's why she's been giving me such a hard time about taking my money. If you can persuade her to change her mind, I'd be eternally grateful to you.'

'Give me time, Carl,' the lawyer replied. 'My motto is to make haste slowly.'

It seemed a tactless remark to make in view of his friend's limited future, but glancing at him, Laura had the impression he had said it deliberately. Duncan himself confirmed this when he rose

A special offer for readers of Mills & Boon
Four Mills & Boon Romances-FREE

We have chosen four Romances for you to enjoy FREE and without obligation as your special introduction to the Mills & Boon Reader Service.

Join the hundreds of readers enjoying Mills & Boon's Reader Service

Take these four free books and you will meet Ravena, about to marry a forbidding stranger to protect her beloved guardian from a terrible secret . . . Sabrina, tragically blinded in an accident, and afraid that the man she loves can offer no more than sympathy . . . Karen, forced to meet the husband she still loves two years after their divorce . . . Caroline, trapped by a misunderstanding that could lead her future husband to believe she deceived him.

Enjoy these moving love stories, and decide for yourself whether you would like to read more. If you would, the Mills & Boon Reader Service allows you to receive the very latest Mills & Boon titles hot from the presses every month, delivered to your door, post and packing free. There are many other exclusive advantages, too:

★ No commitment. You receive books for only as long as you want.
★ No hidden extra charges. Postage and packing is completely free.
★ Friendly, personal attention from Reader Service Editor Susan Welland. Why not call her now on 01-684 2141 if you have any queries?
★ FREE monthly newsletter crammed with competitions, knitting patterns, recipes, bargain book offers, and exclusive special offers for you, your home and your friends.

THE FOUR FREE BOOKS ARE OUR SPECIAL GIFT TO YOU. THEY ARE YOURS TO KEEP WITHOUT ANY OBLIGATION TO BUY FURTHER BOOKS.

You have nothing to lose — and a whole world of romance to gain. See how the Reader Service can help you to enjoy Mills & Boon even more by filling in and posting the coupon today.

Mills & Boon Reader Service, FREEPOST, P.O. Box 236, Croydon, Surrey CR9 9EI

FREE BOOKS CERTIFICATE

To: **Mills & Boon Reader Service, FREEPOST, P.O. Box 236, Croydon, Surrey CR9 9EL.**

Please send me, FREE AND WITHOUT OBLIGATION, the four Mills & Boon Romances illustrated above, and reserve a Reader Service Subscription for me. If I decide to subscribe I shall, from the beginning of the month following my free parcel of books, receive 6 new books each month for £5.70, post and packing free. If I decide not to subscribe, I shall write to you within 14 days. The free books are mine to keep in any case. I understand that I may cancel my subscription at any time simply by writing to you. I am over 18 years of age.

Name _____
(Please write in block capitals).
Address _____

_____

Town_____ County_____

4C36

Postcode _____
Send no money. Take no risks.   No stamp needed.

to take his leave and she went with him to the front door.

'Carl knows his time is short and he wouldn't thank me if I pretended otherwise. Nor would he want me to monitor everything I said, in case it upset him. He's too clever not to see through such tact.' He held out his hand. 'I hope we'll meet again soon. If there's any way in which I can help you, don't hesitate to call me.'

'I don't want Carl to leave me his money or the company,' she said abruptly. 'If you could talk him out of that, I'd be eternally grateful.'

'I appreciate the way you feel, Laura, but sometimes it's harder to accept than to refuse. I know you have your pride, but so has Carl. And that's all he does have. Don't take it away from him.'

She sighed. 'I suppose he told you that himself?'

'He didn't need to. It's obvious.' Duncan Thorpe's expression was speculative. 'Why do you have such a complex about taking anything from him? You have more right to it than anyone else in his life.'

'I don't agree. I married him to—well, you know the reason. If I accepted his money, I'd be no better than Rosemary.'

'You're entirely different from Rosemary.'

'You know her?' Laura asked.

'I met her in New York by chance. She came there after you and Carl got married.'

Laura longed to know what he thought of Rosemary, but training kept her silent, as training kept him from satisfying her curiosity.

'Think over what I've said,' he reiterated. 'If giving you a secure future makes Carl happy, you should swallow your determination to be different from Rosemary, and do as he wishes.'

She was still mulling over this highly charged advice when he got into his car and drove away. Was it only her determination to show Carl she was not another Rosemary that was making her refuse his desire to leave her all his possessions? How would she feel if their marriage was a genuine one?

Without thinking, she knew the question of finance would never have arisen; when true love existed between a man and wife, there was no dividing line between his and hers.

Thoughtfully she closed the front door. She must think carefully what to do.

CHAPTER NINE

To Laura's surprise, Duncan became a frequent visitor to Holly Grove, dining with them once a week and always making up a fourth for bridge on Sunday evening.

With all the will in the world Laura could not simulate an interest in cards, and on a Sunday she and Mary would go to the cinema. Having the nurse in the house was a constant source of comfort, for she was the only person with whom Laura had no need to pretend. When the bitterness she felt towards Rosemary exploded into something verbal, she had no need to monitor her outbursts if Mary was with her, and when her love for Carl depressed her, she did not have to hide it by a false smile.

'It's all such a waste,' she exclaimed one Sunday, when her mood was especially low. 'Why did Carl have to be the one to fall from that scaffolding?'

'That sort of question can never be answered. You should stop thinking about it.'

'I can't.'

'Do you want him to know you love him?'

'Of course not.'

'Then take a good look at yourself in the mirror. If you get any thinner, he'll begin to suspect there's something wrong with you—and it won't take him long to guess what it is. I hate having to use a cliché, but you've got to pull yourself together.'

'How?' Laura asked bitterly. 'Do I run around pretending I'm looking forward to the future!'

'You can at least stop looking as if the end of the world is imminent.'

'It *is* for me.'

There was a momentary silence. 'I'm sorry, Laura. I know how you feel, but since you keep saying you don't want him to know ...'

'Thanks for reminding me,' Laura said. 'Though heaven knows how I can pretend I don't care.'

'Find yourself something to do. Haven't you got a hobby?'

'I haven't had much time for one. Even at weekends I used to take work home from the office.'

'A labour of love,' Mary smiled.

'I never regarded it as labour of any kind. It was extremely interesting work. You don't need to be an architect or an engineer to know if building plans are good or bad. You just need common sense—which most architects don't seem to have!'

'I've heard that comment before!' the nurse quipped.

'It's Carl's favourite one,' Laura smiled. 'Maybe I'll start going to the office with him. At least it will give me something to do.'

To Laura's surprise, Carl refused point blank to let her undertake any of the responsibilities she had once done as his secretary.

'You are my wife and I won't have you acting as anything else,' he declared.

'But I'm bored doing nothing.'

'What do other wives do?'

'They run a home and look after children.' She stopped. 'I'm sorry, Carl, that was a stupid thing to say.'

'It was a normal thing to say.'

They were at the breakfast table, sitting opposite each other in the small room which gave on to the gaily tiled patio. In the summer the patio would catch the early morning sunshine and when the weather became less inclement they would be able to have breakfast there. But Carl would only have one season—at the most two—in which to enjoy it.

'I'm sorry, Carl,' she said again.

'I'm the one who should be sorry,' he said heavily. 'I seem to have done you out of a great deal. You're the type of woman who *should* be taking care of a home and bringing up her children.'

She searched for the right words to say, but he gave her no chance.

'Still, you're young and you'll have plenty of time to have a loving husband and a brood of children to give your life meaning.'

'I wish you wouldn't say that,' she said unhappily.

'Why not? I want to think of your future as a happy one. It gives me pleasure.'

'It doesn't give *me* pleasure!' she cried. 'Please, Carl, I can't bear it when you talk of the future.'

With an enormous effort she prevented herself from running from the table and fiercely concentrated on her breakfast plate, counting every flower in the floral design. Had she given herself away to him? Certainly most men would have guessed how she felt, yet Carl still regarded her as his highly efficient and unemotional secretary—even though he wouldn't let her act as one. All she was was his secretary wife.

'You should see more people of your own age,' he said abruptly. 'You must have had some sort of social life before you married me, but you never invite any of your friends here.'

'I don't have many friends.'

'From choice, I'm sure.'

She shrugged. 'I was an only child and born late in my parents' life. It spoiled me for men and women of my own age. That's why I've always been happier with older people.'

'Like me?' he teased and, pushing his wheelchair away from the table, glided to the window. 'We'll talk about this again later. I have an appointment in the office at ten. You're not to come with me,' he concluded, and went out.

Laura remained at the breakfast table long after he had gone, and was still sitting there when the telephone rang. There was an extension in this room and she picked it up. It was Duncan, asking to speak to Carl.

'You'll be able to reach him at the office in half an hour,' she said.

Duncan thanked her, but instead of hanging up, went on talking.

'You sound unusually subdued, Laura. Is anything wrong?'

'Carl and I were just talking about what I can do to relieve my boredom.'

'You can't be serious! You're far too intelligent to let yourself be bored.'

'But I *am*,' she said wildly. 'Excruciatingly, indescribably bored!'

There was a short silence, as if he was weighing up something. 'Are you free to have lunch with me?' he asked.

'Oh, please,' she said guiltily. 'I didn't mean you to——'

'You'll be doing me a favour,' he cut in. 'One

o'clock at the Stafford.'

She agreed and, putting down the telephone, found herself unaccountably pleased at the prospect of getting out of the house.

At one o'clock she was waiting in the foyer of the Stafford Hotel, feeling elegant in a turquoise jersey dress and coat. Her dark brown hair, newly washed, had a reddish gleam to it and she had brushed it away from her face to fall behind her ears. It was a more sophisticated style than usual, and she was aware of a couple of men eyeing her appreciatively. How easily male attention could be caught. Fine feathers without doubt made fine birds!

'Sorry to be late,' Duncan Thorpe came towards her, 'but I had to do a bit of juggling with my diary.'

'You're making me feel guilty again,' she protested.

'Good. I always like to play on a woman's conscience!'

She laughed and he cupped her elbow and escorted her into the dining room.

'I suggest we have a drink at the table. It's quieter and we can talk.'

'Business?' she queried.

'Certainly not, this is a social lunch.'

He was true to his word and during the meal talked about his stay in New York, which he considered to be one of the most exciting cities in the world.

'It has all the faults that people say it has,' he commented when they reached the coffee stage, 'but it also has a vitality that other cities lack. One feels an urgency to get things done and an eagerness to conquer the world. You don't find that sort of mood here any more.'

Laura was astonished to hear him talk like this, for she had always considered him to be ultra-conservative in his ideas.

'Don't equate my character with my profession,' he said slyly, indicating that he knew exactly what she was thinking. 'You, for example, have always— at least until today—portrayed the perfect private secretary.'

'Even though I'm Carl's wife?'

'You don't act as if you were his wife.'

'Because I don't feel it.' She stirred her sugarless coffee. 'I'm still the same girl I was when I worked for him, and I can't pretend otherwise.'

'Yet you *have* changed. Today you're different from when I first met you.'

'It's the dress,' she said. 'Carl asked me to wear brightly coloured clothes.'

'The fact that you did shows your own desire to change. Also the fact that you're bored. You want to explore a new world and find a new you.'

She smiled. 'Are you a lawyer or a writer?'

'With you I undoubtedly become lyrical!'

They both laughed, but Laura found he had put into words a restlessness she had not clearly under-stood until this moment. It was warming to know that another person was able to express her mood; it made her feel less alone. She gave him another, warmer smile and he echoed it, his thin face creas-ing into many lines. He was not good-looking, but he had a definite charm and an urbane sophistica-tion that added to it. He was less dynamic than Carl, yet in his quiet way he was just as strong.

'Tell me *why* you are bored,' he asked. 'Surely

there are many things you can do to occupy your-self?'

'It isn't only my mind that needs occupying,' she confessed, 'it's my emotions. I need a loving hus-band and children and, like an idiot, I said so to Carl.'

'He didn't need you to tell him that. It's because he's aware of it himself that he wants to leave you well provided for.'

'I don't regret marrying, Carl, you know. Faced with the same decision, I would do it again.'

'That's what makes you a nice girl, Laura. All I can add is that you won't be living this way for long. When Carl is dead——'

'Must *you* talk about it too?' she cried. 'Carl does, and I can't bear it!'

He looked at her for a few seconds and then said: 'A good nurse or doctor tries to remain detached from their patient. You should be well advised to do the same.'

'I'm not Carl's nurse or doctor. For three years he's been a close part of my life.'

'He still doesn't want you to become emotional.'

'What do you suggest I do? Keep a stiff upper lip?'

'That's it exactly. Find yourself a job if need be. But get out of the house and start to live a life of your own.'

'I don't want to be out of the house on a regular basis. I never know when Carl is likely to need me. As time goes on he's bound to get more depressed and—and——'

'And you want to be there?' Duncan patted her hand. 'Very well, Laura, there's only one other thing you can do.'

'What's that?'

'Take the odd evening off and go out with another man.'

'Carl would hate it,' she protested.

'No, he wouldn't. You're a young and lovely woman and you can't hide that fact. Your marriage isn't real, and you're pining for masculine attention.'

Angrily she shook her head. 'I'm not looking for a love affair.'

'I didn't say you were. I said masculine attention. You want to feel you're being seen as a woman.'

It was a perceptive comment, but she was wary of admitting it.

'We're arguing for nothing, Duncan. I don't know any man who would be willing to act as an admiring escort to a married woman who has a "don't touch me" sign round her neck!'

'I do,' he said promptly. 'I'll get him to call you.'

She pretended to search for her compact and dabbed powder on cheeks that were suddenly pink.

'You look even lovelier when you blush,' he said softly and, as she did not answer, he pushed back his chair and rose.

Outside the hotel he saw her into a taxi and paid the driver. 'Thank you for lunching with me, Laura. I enjoyed it very much.'

'I should be the one to thank *you* for taking pity on me. Goodbye, Duncan.'

'Au revoir. It's a more appropriate word for us to use.'

There was no need to ask him what he meant. The look in his eyes told her, and she pondered on it during the long journey back to Holly Grove and hoped she was not going to regret her luncheon with him. She liked Duncan as a friend, nothing more, and it would be embarrassing if he did not realise it.

Carl was delighted when he heard Laura had been out with Duncan and when the lawyer came to dinner a few evenings later, he referred to it.

'I'm glad Laura went out with you. If I don't go to the office, she has a bad habit of hovering round me and being solicitous. I'd be happy for her to get out much more than she does.'

'There you are, Laura,' Duncan said, staring her full in the face. 'Let's fix a date now. You see you have Carl's permission.'

'You'll need my permission too,' she told him, and was glad when the conversation turned to a new contract which Carl was negotiating with a Swedish architect.

But that night, when she was alone with Carl, she asked him why he had deliberately pushed Duncan into asking her out.

'Because it's in your best interest,' he replied. 'Duncan likes you, and it would do you good to go dancing or to the theatre.'

'You can take me to the theatre,' she said quickly.

'I'm not in the mood.'

'Do you think *I* am?'

He was silent, his face half averted so that she saw only his profile, which gave away nothing of his thoughts. 'I like to have cheerful people around me,' he said tonelessly. 'If you stay glued to my side you'll lose your efficacy.'

'I didn't know you wanted me to be your clown!' she said tartly.

'Laura, please.' He leaned forward in his chair,

his jaw set firm. 'Don't you know how guilty I feel at what I've done to your life? I should never have married you.'

'I'm glad you did. I mean it, Carl.'

'That only makes me feel worse for taking advantage of your sympathy. But if I could believe you were having some amusement—that I haven't robbed you of two years of your youth ...'

She hesitated. The best way to stop Carl from being conscience-stricken for spoiling her life was to tell him she had married him because she loved him. But this would make him feel even more guilty and could affect the friendship that had sprung up between them and on which he relied. All she could do was to agree to go out with Duncan, even though she would prefer to spend every waking moment with the man in front of her.

'Very well, Carl. I'll do as you want. But tell me, does your open-mindedness extend only to Duncan?'

'Is there another man you know?' he asked instantly.

'Of course not. The question was academic.'

'I see. For a moment I thought ...' He relaxed and smiled. 'You once told me you have unfathomable depths, but I'd hate to think there was a man swimming around in them!'

'What a Jungian concept!'

He chuckled and unexpectedly reached for her hand. His physical gestures towards her were rare and, since the night of their marriage, he had never kissed her. Now he raised her hand to his lips. 'You're the only woman who has never bored me and the only one who answers me back without losing her temper.'

'No woman would dare to lose her temper with you!' she said, anxious to keep sentiment out of this scene in case she burst into tears.

'You're right,' he agreed. 'Whenever they showed signs of it, I dropped them like a hot potato. I've had to fight so much in my business life that I always wanted things easy in my emotional one.'

'Is that why you went from woman to woman?' she asked.

'They all bored me. They were so obvious in what they wanted.'

'You were pretty obvious too,' she said drily.

'Sexual attraction is a strong motivation.' His voice was equally dry. 'But now it's over. In some ways, that's a relief.'

He released her hand and spun his chair towards the door. Laura ran across to open it for him and he turned as though to stop her. The movement altered the angle of his chair and she knocked against the footrest.

He gave a sharp cry of pain and she bent towards him. His hands were squeezing the arms of the chair and beads of perspiration were erupting on his upper lip. It was incredible that knocking against his chair should cause him such intense pain, and she wondered fearfully if anything else was wrong.

'I'll fetch Mary,' she said swiftly, and raced up the stairs.

By the time she and the nurse returned, Carl was in control of himself. 'You fuss too much, Laura. There's nothing the matter with me.'

'But you were in pain. I saw it.'

'Well, I'm not in pain any more, so forget it.'

But far into the night Laura remembered the agony on his face and wondered fearfully if the two years to live—which Mr Edwards had given him —had been over-optimistic.

CHAPTER TEN

EARLY the next morning Laura went in search of Mary to see how Carl was.

'I don't care what he said last night,' she reiterated. 'I'm sure he was in intense pain. Can't you persuade him to see Mr Edwards again?'

'Mr. Anderson called him a little while ago,' Mary said, 'and he's coming over this morning.'

Though this was exactly what Laura wanted, she was desperately afraid at what the outcome of the visit might be. Without stopping to think, she ran into Carl's bedroom. It was only as she saw his face that she took a hold of herself. To show him how afraid she was would serve no purpose other than to distress him. With an enormous effort, she forced a smile to her lips.

'Good morning, Carl. I came in to see if you're going to the office today.'

'I'm not sure. I'm expecting Mr Edwards here any moment.'

'Here?' she asked with pretended surprise.

'Yes. There's no point in you and me having any secrets about my health. That attack last night might be the beginning—or perhaps I should say the beginning of the end.'

'I think you're being unnecessarily pessimistic.'

'I'd believe that more easily if you didn't look so tragic.' The brusqueness of Carl's tone made her take control of herself.

'I'm sorry, Carl. I—I've never been good at acting.'

Even as she spoke she knew what a lie this was. Her ability to hide her love for this big, silver blond man was the greatest performance any woman could have given.

'Smile at me,' he ordered.

Obediently she curved her mouth and hoped he did not see the bleakness in her eyes. 'Would you mind if I spoke to Mr Edwards after he's seen you?' she asked.

'Most wives do,' Carl shrugged.

'My position is somewhat different.'

'Very different,' he agreed. 'And because of it, you have every right to talk to Mr Edwards.' He patted the bed. 'Come and sit beside me.'

Nervously she did so and Carl put his hand on hers.

'Don't look so scared, Laura. I'm not going to bite you. I just want to have you close.' He pulled her nearer. 'I never had a sister. Perhaps if I had, I might be more understanding of the way women feel.'

Her pleasure dissolved like snow in the sun, but she was careful not to show it. 'You've been very understanding with me, Carl.'

'Have I?' His look was wry. 'I suppose that comes from our sharing a home; and then you know all about my work—which means I can talk to you about my problems. It's funny, but sometimes I——'

He stopped as there was a tap at the door and Mary came in, saw her patient was respectable and then opened the door wider to usher in the surgeon.

Laura murmured a greeting and went out. She remained in the downstairs hall, unwilling to go into the drawing room in case the specialist left without her hearing him. The examination seemed to take a long time and she was in a state of agitation by the time she saw Mr Edwards coming towards her. She led him at once into the drawing room where coffee was waiting and, when she had poured him a cup, asked as emotionlessly as she could whether Carl's illness was progressing faster than he had anticipated.

'I cannot answer that question until I've done a more detailed examination of your husband,' he replied. 'I've arranged for him to be taken into hospital today.' He saw Laura change colour and added quickly: 'Please don't be so distressed. Things may not be as bad as you believe.'

'But *you* must think they are or you wouldn't be taking him to the hospital so quickly.'

'You're misunderstanding me,' he assured her. 'I want to do some special tests, and they require a general anaesthetic.'

'How soon will you have the results?'

'A couple of days.' He set his coffee cup on the trolley. 'Don't show him how worried you are, Mrs Anderson. He relies on your calmness.'

Laura remembered this when she returned to Carl's room. True to her expectation, he made only a fleeting reference to his departure to the hospital, though he could not disguise his pallor. He was a highly intelligent man and undoubtedly knew what the results of these tests might be.

Carl's stay in hospital was longer than Mr Edwards had said, and two days became ten. Carl was disturbed at the thought of Laura spending all her time with him and insisted she went out several times with Duncan. Knowing that to remonstrate with him would be bad for his peace of mind, she did as he asked, glad that she liked Duncan well enough not to be embarrassed at having him co-opted as her escort. The thought was wryly amusing. She regarded Duncan almost as a brother while Carl saw her as the sister he had never had. What a pity she could not see Carl as a brother too!

'Have you given any thought to what you'll do when Carl dies?' Duncan asked, driving her home one evening after a visit to the theatre.

'I don't want to think about it,' Laura said shortly.

'You should.'

'I suppose I'll travel,' she said slowly. 'I had made arrangements to leave Carl when he married Rose-mary, but after his accident I decided to stay.'

'Ah yes. Carl mentioned you'd been going to leave him.'

She glanced at Duncan and knew from his expression that he had not guessed the real reason why she had wanted to leave Carl.

'Do you have any particular country in mind?' Duncan asked.

'I thought of going to Australia and then perhaps to America.'

'Why not make it America first? I have the chance of taking over the New York office permanently.'

The news surprised her, for Duncan seemed too English to settle anywhere else.

'Lawyers are the same breed no matter where they are,' he remarked jokingly as she put her thoughts into words. 'I'm as happy working on the other side of the Atlantic as I am here. The only reason I haven't gone back to the States before now is because I wanted to be with you.'

'I know Carl is extremely glad you're here,' she said hurriedly.

'I'm not remaining here because of Carl,' Duncan replied, 'and you know it. I'm in love with you and I want——'

'No, Duncan, don't go on.'

'I must. I want you to be my wife.'

'I'm Carl's wife,' she said angrily. 'How can you ask me to be yours?'

'I'm not a hypocrite,' he said firmly. 'Would you have preferred me to wait until Carl is dead before telling you how I feel? That would have been far worse—to wait for a man to die before admitting that you covet his wife! Besides, you aren't his wife in the real sense.'

'That has nothing to do with it!'

Duncan pulled into the kerb and stopped the car. 'Don't forget Rosemary. If it were not for her, Carl would never have married you.'

'Do you think I can forget that?' she said bitterly.

'I'm not sure. You seem to see yourself as his guardian—the light in his darkness. But you're not. You're only a safety barrier for him; the woman who's keeping Rosemary at bay. He's *using* you, Laura, and he feels guilty about it. That's why he wants you to lead your own life. If you don't believe me, ask him yourself.'

'I don't need to,' she whispered, keeping her head down. 'He's already said as much to me.'

'Then what more do you want?' Duncan slid across the seat and put his arm lightly across her shoulders. 'I know you don't love me, but you like me and we get on well together. I'm sure that once you're free you'll start to give vent to your real feelings.'

With all her heart Laura realised that what Duncan said was true. But unhappily it was the exact opposite. Carl's death would not leave her free to love someone else but would put her into a state of perpetual mourning. It was hard enough to lose someone with whom you shared happiness, but to lose them without ever having the chance of finding happiness with them only heightened one's sense of loss. Yet she dared not say this to Duncan for fear he told Carl.

'We won't talk about it any more,' he murmured, pressing his lips to her temple. 'I only want you to know I love you and that one day I hope you will be my wife.'

Without waiting for her reply, he released her and set the car in motion. They drove the rest of the way in silence and at the front door he caught her hand and held it tightly.

'May I see you tomorrow, Laura? I've got papers for Carl to sign and I can meet you at the hospital.'

'I don't want to go out with you tomorrow, Duncan.'

'I have tickets for the Festival Hall,' he reminded her. 'You said you wanted to hear a concert performance of *Der Rosenkavalier*.'

'You make it difficult for me to refuse.'

'Good. In that respect I'm like Carl. We're both men who won't take no for an answer.'

'Birds of a feather,' she said with an effort at lightness. 'Is that why you're such good friends?'

'Possibly. We trust each other too. That's more important than anything else.'

'Then don't betray his trust!' she said suddenly.

'Do you think I would?' Duncan asked sharply. 'Carl knows I love you. I told him so!'

'You had no right,' she cried.

'But he's delighted by it. It's what he's been hoping for!'

This was more than Laura could take in, and muttering goodnight, she ran into the house. Was Duncan telling the truth? Did Carl feel such remorse at having tied her to him—even for such a short time—that his conscience could only be appeased if he believed that marriage to him had enabled her to meet the one man she could truly loved? Or did he have such a sense of responsibility towards her that he could only rest easy if he knew her future was assured with a man in whom he had implicit trust? Either way it was unthinkable. She did not love Duncan and not even for Carl could she contemplate being his wife.

At mid-morning the following day a bouquet of red roses arrived for her and, seeing them, she was reminded of the time when Carl had sent Rosemary a hundred golden ones. 'He's never sent *me* any flowers,' she thought, and was so annoyed with her self-pity that she fussed over Duncan's flowers as if they meant something to her. If only one could fall in love to order—how simple everything would be.

She was thinking of this when she entered Carl's room in the hospital and at once noticed the row of new novels on the window ledge.

'From Duncan,' he told her, intercepting her glance.

'He's certainly been busy this morning,' she said, and regretted her words as Carl raised an eyebrow.

'Don't tell me he's sent *you* books as well?'

'Flowers,' she murmured. 'You know how—how punctilious he is about doing the right thing.'

'Duncan didn't send flowers out of politeness. He's in love with you.'

She felt her face grow warm and knew from the gleam in Carl's eyes that he had noticed it.

'Don't try and fool me,' he continued. 'We've always been honest with each other. I'm glad he's in love with you. It's what I've wanted.'

'You're unflatteringly eager to be rid of me.' Even as she spoke, she knew how silly her words were. Here was Carl trying to be as honest as he knew how, while she was shying away from the truth like a startled colt. Yet try as she could, it was impossible for her to be as fatalistic about the future as this big, quietly controlled man lying in the bed in front of her.

'Rogers came to see me this morning.' Abruptly Carl reverted to business. 'He's leaving the company and joining Mastins.'

'The enemy camp,' she said indignantly.

'They're welcome to him. I've been angling for his resignation for months ...'

'Whatever for?'

'Because you don't like him—though you still haven't told me what he said to you that day when he called you into his office. Will you tell me now?'

'It's so long ago I've forgotten it,' she lied.

'Well, I haven't. I can still see the look on your face when I found you leaning against the wall. There and then I made up my mind to make things so difficult for him that he would resign without my having to have a boardroom row to get rid of him. It took a bit of manoeuvring,' he added grimly, 'but I did it.'

Though she knew he could be ruthless when it suited him, it was a shock to have it so openly displayed, and she was glad she was not his enemy. Yet with women he must have a different attitude, for Rosemary—who deserved his most venomous dislike—seemed not to have aroused it.

'What thoughts are going on behind those big brown eyes of yours?' he questioned and, as always when he paid her a compliment she was thrown into confusion. Confusion, this time, made her blurt out exactly what she *had* been thinking.

'I don't feel venomous towards Rosemary,' he said after a short pause. 'In a way I'm sorry for her.'

'*Sorry?*'

His smile was bitter. 'I could have made her so happy, and she missed it all!'

Jealousy stabbed Laura like a knife. Despite Rosemary's heartless rejection of him after his accident and her blatant return when she had learned that his days were numbered—Carl still hankered for the happiness he believed he could have had with her. Didn't he know that one-way love could never bring genuine fulfilment? The urge to tell him this trembled on her lips, but as she went to speak he moved restlessly and the blankets shifted on his legs. Seeing their inert outline she was filled with such compassion that all jealousy died. Poor Carl! Let him continue with his dreams; they were all he had.

'Sorry to disturb you, Mr Anderson.' A nurse came in and stood starched and efficient at the end of the bed. 'Mr Edwards is on his way up and I would like to prepare you.'

'I'll wait outside,' Laura murmured.

'It will be a long examination,' the nurse informed her.

'Then I'll go and do some window-shopping and come back later.'

Hiding the fear that the nurse's words had aroused, Laura debated whether to wait and see the surgeon, then decided to hear what Carl had to tell her first. She could always telephone Mr Edwards later that evening.

Forcing her mind into a state of limbo, she spent the next hour looking at the shops in the Burlington Arcade. She bought herself a sweater she did not want, because she knew it would please Carl when she showed it to him, and returned to the hospital as the tea trays were being taken down the corridor.

'You must have smelled the scones,' a nurse said cheerfully to her. 'I've just served your husband his tea, but I'll bring you another cup.'

Smiling her thanks, Laura went into his room. Carl's face was flushed and the fear she had been trying to control flooded out. Dropping the parcel and her bag to the floor, she ran across to his bed.

'What did Mr Edwards say? How much worse is it? Tell me the truth, Carl, I want to know!'

His hand gripped her shoulder painfully. 'I'm not going to die yet, Laura, and when I do, it will more than likely be from natural causes.'

Her breath caught in her throat and she stared at him wordlessly.

'The earlier findings were wrong,' he continued. 'Either that, or a miracle has happened. And since I don't believe in miracles, I can only assume that somebody doing those tests made one hell of a mistake!'

Laura went on staring at him. There were many

things she wanted to ask, but her tongue refused to move. All she could do was absorb the wonderful, unbelievable fact that he was not going to die in two years or less. Unfortunately this did not mean he would be able to walk again, but at least he would live a normal span of life.

'It's come as a shock to you,' he said gently, and moved his fingers in a tentative gesture along the side of her neck. She longed to catch hold of his hand and cradle it against her breast, and held herself so rigid—in case she gave way to this desire— that he immediately felt her tension and took his hand away.

'It's been a shock to me too,' he added. 'You face the unbelievable fact that you're going to die soon —you almost come to terms with it—and then you find you aren't going to be snuffed out like a candle but will live for years as a helpless log!'

'You aren't helpless.' She found her voice at last. 'And you mustn't be sorry about it! It's the most wonderful news in the world.'

'What's wonderful about being a hulk in a wheel-chair?'

'You aren't a hulk. You've made yourself so mobile that half the time people forget you can't walk.'

'*I* don't forget.'

His voice was almost inaudible and he leaned back against the pillows. His skin was still flushed and it robbed him of his years and made him look like a boy. How pale and silver his eyes were beneath their dark lashes, and what desolation lurked in their depths.

'You know what this means, don't you, Laura?'

Not sure she did, Laura shook her head.

'It means you won't be free of me in two years,' he said.

'Oh, Carl!' She longed to jump for joy at the prospect of being with him for a lifetime, but no reaction showed on her face as she moved away from the bed and sat in a chair.

'I can think of worse fates than being tied to you,' she said calmly.

'I can't. You're young and you should be married to a man who can make you happy. You and Duncan are right for each other ...' He banged his hand on the counterpane. 'Why did this have to happen?'

'How can you say that?' Anger brought her to her feet. 'You've been given back your life! You should go down on your knees and thank God for it—not moan because you're married to *me*!'

'I'm not thinking about *my* being tied. It's you!'

'Forget *me* and think about yourself. You must start your physiotherapy again and increase your exercises. You've got to concentrate on walking again—even if it will be with crutches.'

'Spare me false hopes,' he said bitterly. 'It's still your most naïve characteristic.'

Laura swallowed hard. Carl was overwrought and did not mean to hurt her. She was still struggling for composure when a nurse came into the room.

'I just want to plug in your telephone, Mr Anderson.' At his uncomprehending look, she added: 'We always unplug it when a specialist is expected. Particularly with someone like yourself, who's always getting calls.' She lifted the receiver. 'There's one on the line for you now.'

He looked in two minds whether or not to take it, then did so. 'Anderson here.' As he spoke his expression changed, the eyebrows coming together and then moving apart, the hand that was not holding the telephone clenching and unclenching. 'Rosemary!' he exclaimed, and then listened in silence for a long moment. 'Of course you may see me,' he said finally. 'In an hour, then.' He replaced the receiver and gave Laura a narrow glance. 'That was Rosemary. She flew in from New York yesterday and somebody told her I was in hospital.'

Laura was glad she had gone to stand by the window while Carl was speaking, for she could stare out at the chimney tops and not have to look into his face. 'I didn't think you would want to see her again after the way she behaved.'

'It isn't mature to go on bearing a grudge,' he said sardonically. 'Besides, I find it restful to be with women I know—and I can truthfully say that you and Rosemary are two that I know like an open book.'

'Rosemary possibly,' she said coldly, 'but not me.' Blindly she turned to the chair where her handbag lay. 'You won't mind if I don't stay to welcome her? I'm not in the mood for her tears of joy when she discovers you're going to live.'

'You think there'll be tears of joy?' he asked. 'How do you think Rosemary would have felt if *she* had been married to me instead of you?'

Temper brought Laura swinging round to glare at him. 'Why conjecture about the might-have-been when you can think of what *has* been! Or don't you want to remember that the last time you were in hospital she ran away because she couldn't face life tied to a husband in a wheelchair!'

'You don't need to remind me of that,' he retorted.

'Then how about remembering that she was pre-pared to come back and do a two-year stretch—so long as it wasn't going to be for longer! If you can forget that, you can forget anything!'

Choking with emotion, she stumbled from the room and banged the door behind her.

CHAPTER ELEVEN

LAURA did not know what transpired between Rosemary and Carl, for he returned home the following day and made no reference to her visit.

Because of this, it came as a shock to learn that the girl was remaining in London. Laura knew it could only be at Carl's behest, and she was furious with him for being so weak. Or was it that his love for her was too strong for him to fight? How would she herself feel about Carl if she learned he had done something that filled her with disgust? Even if she knew him to be a scoundrel she was convinced it would not affect her love for him. As Rosemary's behaviour had not affected his love for *her*.

Only to Duncan did she confide her dismay at Carl's behaviour.

'You've already met Rosemary,' she said. 'Were you taken in by her?'

'You know I wasn't. But then she isn't my type and I didn't fall in love with her.'

'Are you saying that love is blind?'

'Sometimes.'

'But Carl knows what she is—that she ran away and left him.'

'Then he loves her despite her faults. Maybe he's the kind of man who wants nothing more from a woman than sexual satisfaction.'

'What a sickening thing to say!'

Duncan shrugged and helped himself to a roll. They had been to a concert and were having a snack in a West End hotel. 'You know, Laura, for an intelligent woman, you're surprisingly naïve.'

'That's what Carl says. But I'm not ashamed of it. If sex can make a man lose his reason, then I still say it's sickening. How can a man want to make love to a woman when his brain tells him she's contemptible?'

'When a man wants to make love to a woman, he isn't concerned with his brain!' Duncan said drily. 'Face facts. Men are notoriously stupid where women are concerned.'

Since Carl had been exceptionally so with herself, Laura was forced to agree.

'Has he said anything to you about wanting a divorce?' she asked.

'You know I can't answer that. If Carl talks to me, it's in a client-lawyer capacity.'

'I'm sorry, I shouldn't have asked.'

'But that doesn't stop me talking to you about *your* plans,' he went on.

'I haven't any plans.'

'Then you should start making some. You can't remain tied to Carl for the rest of your life. That wasn't the basis on which you married him.'

'He hasn't asked me to leave yet.'

'But he made a two-year bargain with you.'

She shook her head. 'I was to be his wife in order to prevent him from making a fool of himself over Rosemary.'

'You're being highly successful at that!' he said sarcastically. 'For heaven's sake, Laura, I love you and I want to marry you. I was prepared to wait until Carl had ... But I can't wait a lifetime—and 'neither can you.'

'I don't love you, Duncan.' She was blunt because she knew she had to be. 'I never told you I do.'

'But you don't love anyone else, and once you're free, you'll feel differently about me. I'm sure of it.'

She lowered her eyes. Short of telling him how she felt about Carl, she could not stop him from planning his future around her. But if he learned the truth, he might tell Carl, who was altruistic enough to have her remain his wife for as long as she wished; seeing this as his only way of repaying her for her willingness to marry him when he had begged her to do so.

'You haven't answered my question,' Duncan said. 'Are you and Carl going to get your marriage annulled?'

'Annulled?' The word caught in her mind, like a fly in a web.

'The marriage wasn't real,' he said patiently, 'so you wouldn't need to go through the indignity of a divorce.'

'Carl might think it more of an indignity to have an annulment.'

'How you end your marriage is unimportant. My one concern is that you do.'

'I haven't said I would marry *you*,' she reminded him, and marvelled again at his inability to recognise the truth. But then, having seen how blind Carl was over Rosemary, she could not blame Duncan for being blind over herself. But sooner or later she must do as he said and clarify her position with Carl. If he wanted her to remain his wife she would joyfully agree, but if he wished to have his freedom ... Well, she would have to agree to that too.

When they reached Holly Grove she saw that the

lights were still on in the library. Instinctively she knew Rosemary was there and wondered if she should ask Duncan to come in. But this was the coward's way out. Sooner or later she must meet Rosemary, and when she did, she would rather not have Duncan's watchful brown eyes on her.

'I'll call you tomorrow,' he said, and kissed her on the brow.

It was his regular way of leaving her, but tonight he also put his arms around her and let his lips travel from her forehead to her mouth. She made a pretence of responding to him, hoping that if she pretended hard enough, she might actually feel something. But though she did not fool herself that she had, she seemed to fool him, for with a sigh of satisfaction, he lifted his face from hers and stared into her eyes.

'You see, you aren't as indifferent to me as you pretend. Once you accept the fact that you no longer owe Carl any loyalty, you'll realise you must ask him for your freedom.'

Without replying Laura went into the hall and closed the door. It took her a moment to regain her composure, then she dropped her coat on to a chair and peered at her reflection in a mirror. Nerves had given her a high colour and made her eyes sparkle. It made her look more spirited and less docile—which, she thought wryly, was just as well.

Resisting the impulse to knock on the library door and warn the occupants that she was coming in, she turned the handle and stepped inside.

Carl was sitting on the settee, a rug across his legs. In the evening Max usually placed him there and wheeled away the chair, only returning with it when Carl wanted to go to bed. Laura wondered if he preferred the settee because it was more comfortable or because it made him forget he could not walk. At this precise moment it had the advantage of enabling Rosemary to nestle against him, which she was now blatantly doing.

'I hope I'm not disturbing you?' Laura made her voice light and amused.

'Rosemary is just leaving,' Carl said.

'Am I?' Rosemary pouted.

'I'm afraid so, my dear. I don't like going to bed too late. It means keeping Max up till all hours.'

He gave Rosemary a gentle push and, as his head turned, Laura saw a lipstick mark on the side of his mouth. She knew Rosemary had seen it too, for the china blue eyes looked at her with triumph.

'Did you have a lovely evening with Duncan?' she asked in a little-girl voice.

'The concert was excellent,' Laura said.

Rosemary stood up. She had slipped off her shoes and she wandered round the room looking for them. Her movements were graceful and with her long blonde hair and flowing green silk dress, she looked as artless as a water nymph.

'Here they are!' she cried, and dangled two silver sandals in her hand before dropping them to the ground and stepping into them. 'Will you call me in the morning, Carl?'

'I'll be busy in the morning.'

'Then I'll expect to hear from you in the afternoon.' She blew him a kiss from the door and then looked at Laura. 'Do you think you could get me a radio cab?'

Laura longed to say she was no longer Carl's secretary, but knew that to show anger would be playing into Rosemary's hands. Silently she did as she was asked, aware of Carl watching her.

'A taxi will be here in a couple of minutes,' she said, replacing the receiver.

'Do show me out,' Rosemary smiled.

'That will be a pleasure.' Laura moved to the door and caught the twinkle in Carl's eyes. How dared he be so amused? Did he enjoy pitting one woman against the other like a couple of fighting cocks? Despite her anger, the humorous picture this evoked made her lips twitch and she clamped them firmly together. 'I can hear the taxi,' she said, and walked across the hall.

Rosemary slipped her arms into a silver grey mink coat. 'Do you like it, Laura? I bought it because it's the same colour as Carl's eyes.'

'You should have chosen a green one—to remind you of his money!'

The blue eyes glittered, but the voice remained husky. 'I know you hate me for leaving him after the accident, but I have a phobia about sick people.'

'Then why did you come back?' Laura demanded.

'Because I realised how wrong I was. I hoped Carl would forgive me and take me back.'

'After the way you behaved?'

'He *would* have taken me back if it hadn't been for you!' Rosemary cried. 'But you incited him against me.'

'I did nothing of the sort.'

'You did! You loved him and you saw your chance of getting him. From the minute I came into his office and saw the way you looked at him, I knew you'd do anything you could to take him away from me.'

'I didn't need to do anything,' Laura said fiercely.

'It was *your* callousness that made you lose him.'

'And how quickly you stepped into the breach!' Rosemary's voice rose. 'I would have got him back if you hadn't been hanging around like a leech. But you won't keep him for long. He loves me, *me*!'

Laura wrenched open the front door and, as Rosemary stepped over the threshold, she slammed it shut. Shakily she sped across the hall to the stairs, but with her hand on the banister, she stopped. Carl was sitting on the couch, too far away from the bell to ring for Max. Furious though she was with him, she did not have the heart to leave him there, waiting to be picked up like a parcel. Bracing herself to face him, she returned to the library.

At her entrance he tilted his head enquiringly.

'Shall I call Max for you?' she asked.

'Not for the moment.' He folded his arms across his chest. 'Why didn't Duncan come in with you?'

'I didn't ask him.'

Laura moved to warm her hands by the fire and again saw the lipstick mark on the side of his mouth. Reaching for her handbag, she took out a tissue and handed it to him.

'Rosemary has branded you,' she said tonelessly.

Obediently he wiped at his cheek. 'Has it gone?'

She nodded without speaking and he crumpled the tissue into a ball and threw it into the fire.

'Stop looking like the wrath of the gods, Laura,' he said lightly.

His humorous tone made her temper rise and overflow. 'Do you expect me to dance for joy because you're letting Rosemary make a fool of you again?'

131

She swung round to leave him and, not looking where she was going, stumbled over the edge of the rug that was covering his legs. He put out his hand to steady her and she clutched at it, but when she went to draw away he pulled her down until she was on the settee beside him.

'Off with the old and on with the new,' she said tautly.

'Be quiet,' he said. 'Be quiet and kiss me.'

Startled, she stared at him and, with a speed that surprised her, he pushed her back against the cushions and pressed his mouth hard on hers. It was a kiss that held no tenderness, only a pent-up longing that he could no longer hold in check. Again and again his mouth drained hers and though she tried to resist him, she soon found that her need of him was making her defence a weak and puny thing. Bitterly she knew she was coming in for the backlash of emotion which Rosemary had left unsatisfied. When she was alone she would hate herself for not fighting him, but at least she would have a memory to dwell on in the dismal future. Winding her arms around his neck, she pulled him closer.

Feeling her response, the pressure of his mouth softened. His body was trembling and the weight of it was heavy upon her, pushing her deeper into the softness of the settee. One arm lay behind her and unexpectedly he used it to raise himself and look deep into her eyes.

'You're very sweet, Laura. Sweeter than I dreamed.'

She gazed back at him, wishing she could find a deeper meaning in his words. Of course she was sweet. She had married him to help him keep free of Rosemary and she was letting him kiss her for the same reason. In every way she was a paragon of wives.

'I don't find it flattering to be used as a stand-in,' she said evenly, and saw the silver grey irises darken as though a shadow were passing over them.

'Stand-in?' he echoed.

'Why else are you kissing me? You still love Rosemary and I'm still your best way of fighting her. I don't mind,' she said coolly, 'but don't let us pretend it's anything more. After all, I married you knowing the truth, and I have no regrets about it.'

'Even though you know it's going to be for longer than two years?' he questioned.

'So what?' Deliberately she made her voice light, surprised at how uncaring it sounded.

It surprised him too, for he pulled away completely and rested against the corner of the settee. As he sat there, the rug tumbled around him, his hair awry, it was hard to believe he could not stand up and walk. She tried not to think of this, afraid that the knowledge would weaken her into showing her love for him.

'I enjoy being married to you, Carl. I have a beautiful home, plenty of money to spend and no one to tell me what to do.'

'A full and varied life,' he said bitterly.

'As full and varied as I require.'

'When are you seeing Duncan again?'

The question was unexpected, but she took it in her stride. 'Why are you so curious to know? Are you hoping I'll fall in love with him and leave you?'

'You need love.'

'That wasn't what I asked,' she said quietly. 'If

you want me to go, all you have to do is to tell me.'

'Of course I don't want you to go!' Carl spoke so fast that the words seemed to rush out. 'But I feel guilty for tying you to me. It was supposed to be for two years, Laura, not a lifetime.'

'I'll let you know when I want to leave,' she said. 'Now can we stop talking about it?'

'Just one thing more.' Carl's eyes were two probing points of grey. 'Has Duncan asked you to marry him?'

Her sharp, indrawn breath gave him his answer and he leaned back against the settee. 'What did you tell him?'

'I said no.'

'Out of loyalty to me?'

'Partly,' she lied, 'and partly because I don't love him.'

'Don't?' he asked. 'Or won't?'

She was silent. Carl's persistence puzzled her. Did his desire to have her leave him stem from a wish to have her live a fulfilled life, or did it come from his own personal regret at having married her?

'I'm damned if I'm going to die and leave Rosemary a rich widow!' he had once said. But things had changed since then and he might now want to make her his wife.

'What are you thinking of?' he asked, breaking into her thoughts.

'Of you. You say you feel guilty for spoiling my life, but wouldn't it be more true to say you're concerned with the way you've spoiled your own?'

Surprisingly he laughed. 'I like you when you're being sharp. It's a departure from the norm.'

'You haven't answered my question. If you were free, would you marry Rosemary?'

'The bell,' he replied. 'Would you ring for Max? I'm tired and want to go to bed.'

Silently she did his bidding and, still in silence, left the room.

She slept badly that night and the next morning had breakfast in bed, an unprecedented thing for her to do. It also brought Carl to her room for the first time, and she stared in astonishment as he wheeled himself in.

'Is anything wrong?' she asked.

'That's what I came to ask *you*. Max said you were still in bed and I thought that you were ill.'

'It's only an attack of lazybones. I'm sorry if it alarmed you.' She lowered her eyes to her coffee, but was aware of him wheeling his chair to the window and staring into the garden.

'You don't have a good view from here,' he said abruptly. 'You should have given me this room and taken mine.'

'That wouldn't have been right.'

'Why not? You're my wife.'

Unwilling for the conversation to follow the same line it had taken last night, she said nothing.

'I have something to tell you, Laura,' he murmured. 'I should have told you last night, but . . .'

Laura did not hear the rest of what he said. There was a rushing sound in her ears and a blur of red in front of her eyes. So it had come at last! He was going to admit he could no longer fight his need for Rosemary. What a fool she was to have thought it could be otherwise!

'Haven't you any comment to make?' he asked.

'What can I say?'

'Whether you approve or not.'

'Do you seriously expect me to approve?' she

cried. 'It seems to me that what you're doing has been inevitable. The only wonder is that you've resisted it for so long.'

'I would hardly describe a week as being long.'

'A week?' She was puzzled.

'Not even a complete week,' he replied. 'Six days, actually. That was when Mr Edwards had a reply from Vanberg.'

Only then did Laura realise they were talking at cross purposes. Yet she dared not admit she had not heard a word lest Carl thought there was something wrong with her. Perhaps if she phrased the next few questions carefully she might fathom out what he had said.

'I've asked Mr Edwards to make the arrangements as soon as possible,' Carl continued. 'He's hoping Vanberg will fly over at the end of next week. If he can't, and wants to delay it, then I'll fly to Seattle.'

'Why Seattle?'

'Because that's where he has his clinic. He has apparently worked miracles for people with exactly the same condition as mine.'

Laura swallowed hard. At last she was beginning to understand. Vanberg was a surgeon and going to operate on Carl. There was every possibility he would walk again. If that were the case, he would be able to marry Rosemary and keep her happy.

'You don't seem very pleased, Laura.' The chair glided across the carpet and came to a stop by the bed. Carl wore a pale grey sweater and slacks almost the same colour as his eyes. The casual dress made him look more carefree, though this could have been due to the knowledge that he might not be tied to four wheels for much longer.

'It sounds a dangerous operation,' she murmured.

'Vanberg has done many of them.'

'What happens if it isn't successful?'

'I'm back where I started.'

'When will you know if he's coming over?'

'Some time today. The longer I have to wait, the more nervous I feel. I never realised I was a coward until——'

'You aren't a coward! You're desperate to walk again and you want to find out as quickly as possible if you can. That's logic, not cowardice.'

He touched her hand, his expression tender. 'I can always rely on you to say the right thing.'

'You make me sound like man's best friend,' she said wryly.

'You're certainly mine. If I——' He broke off as Mary Roberts came in.

'Mr Edwards' secretary just telephoned,' she said. 'Mr Vanberg will be here in eight days and he wants you to go into hospital a week before, for additional tests. That means tomorrow.'

'I have a board meeting tomorrow,' Carl said. 'I can't put it off.' He frowned. 'I'd better get Durban to chair it for me.' His fingers flexed, as if he was using the movement in lieu of being able to use his legs. 'What a miracle it will be if Vanberg is successful. I know I shouldn't bank on it, but——' he hesitated. 'Is it better to be pessimistic or optimistic?'

'I would rather you were realistic,' Mary replied. 'That way you won't get upset if it doesn't work.'

He banged the arm of his chair. 'What a lot of problems it will solve if I can stand up and push this behind me. I'd give ten years of my life if I knew I'd be able to do that!'

'Don't give away ten years so quickly,' Laura said. 'When you're rushing from one country to another in three months' time, you'll want every one of those ten years you're so ready to give away now.'

He gave a boyish laugh. 'I would settle for limping along—let alone rushing.'

'You'll settle for nothing except a complete cure,' Mary said crisply.

'Heaven spare me from women who know me!' he retorted, and spun his chair to the door. 'I'll see you later, Laura,' he called, and disappeared down the corridor in the direction of the lift.

Mary hesitated on the threshold and Laura beckoned her to come in.

'I suppose you've known about this operation since it was in the offing?'

'Yes.' Mary leaned against the foot of the bed. 'I'm sorry I couldn't tell you——'

'Don't apologise. You're Carl's nurse and your first loyalty is to him.'

'Speaking of loyalty,' Mark said, 'I can't understand how he can see the iron butterfly again. It isn't as if he doesn't know what she is.'

'He knows, but he doesn't care,' Laura sighed.

'I'm glad I decided to settle for a career,' Mary grunted, 'it's far less wearing on the nervous system!' She took the tray from Laura's lap. 'Try and have a sleep: you've got bags under your eyes.'

'Thanks for telling me.'

'That's what friends are for!'

Laura lay back on the pillows but made no attempt to sleep; her mind was too busy going over all Carl had said about the operation. She was by no means sure he had told her the truth and decided to ask Mr Edwards. But even if the operation was dangerous, did she have the right to try and stop him having it? Edgily she flung off the bedclothes and went into the bathroom. She stared at her reflection as she ran the bath. Mary was right, she did look pale and tired. More like a sparrow today than a robin redbreast. The thought brought tears to her eyes, and this, more than anything else, told her how tightly strung her nerves were. Living with a man and having to hide her love for him was hard enough to do without having the additional strain of Rosemary's unwelcome presence. Damn her for coming back to England!

Steam blurred her reflection and Laura turned off the tap and slid into the bath. No matter how dangerous the operation was, Carl was going to have it, for she knew with certainty that only if he could walk again would he allow Rosemary to remain with him. If the operation failed, then he would turn to his good old stand-in—the ever-faithful Laura. Her anger rose and immediately died. How cruel she was being to Carl. If the operation failed he wouldn't want *anyone* to remain with him. She had only to remember the way he was pushing her on to Duncan to recognise the truth of this.

'I'll never leave him alone,' she whispered. 'No matter how many times he tells me to go, I'll never leave him. Only if he goes to Rosemary ...'

Tears trickled down her cheeks and plopped into the water; tears for Carl and tears for herself.

CHAPTER TWELVE

So much seemed to have happened to Laura since she had said goodnight to Duncan that when he called her in the afternoon it was hard to believe barely twelve hours had elapsed. He apparently knew Carl was going into the hospital the next day and that Dr Vanberg was flying from Seattle to perform an operation.

'I've to come to the house with some papers for him to sign,' he explained. 'I hope you'll let me take you out to dinner afterwards?'

'I don't think it's wise for us to meet so often,' said Laura.

'I'll answer that when I see you,' Duncan said, and hung up.

But he was forestalled in this by alighting from his car at precisely the same time as Rosemary alighted from a cab and Laura, walking across the hall as the butler opened the door, saw them come in together. There was something so possessive in the way Rosemary handed her coat to José that Laura longed to reach out and shake her. Instead she gave her a cool smile and led the way into the study where Carl was looking at some plans laid out upon his desk.

He greeted his visitors and signalled Duncan and Rosemary to help themselves to a drink. He had changed into his evening attire. Since his accident he did not wear a dinner jacket, saying he found it too constricting, and instead wore a velvet one. Tonight it was burgundy, with a silk-faced collar and cuffs. It made his hair more golden, and by contrast, Duncan looked thin and dark. But his narrow face was as alert as always, and Laura went to stand beside him as he poured the drinks.

'I *will* go out with you,' she murmured.

'Leaving Rosemary a clear field?' he murmured back.

'It's obviously what Carl wants,' she replied, and during the evening ahead made a determined effort not to think of Carl and Rosemary dining alone together. But it was impossible to keep her mind completely clear and from time to time she pictured them on the settee and wondered if he would push Rosemary back against the cushions and make love to her. The image was so clear and painful that she felt physically ill, and in an effort to concentrate on something other than this, she stared intently at Duncan.

'Has anything happened to you since I saw you last night?' he asked. 'You seem different.'

'I'm a day older.'

'And a day wiser?'

'Much wiser than that.'

He gave her a quizzical look. 'Do I take it that you've given some thought to *our* future?'

'In a way,' she hedged. 'But I don't want to talk about it for the moment. Carl is having this operation and——'

'I understand,' Duncan said quickly. 'I'm quite happy to leave things the way they are for the moment.'

After dinner they went dancing. Ducan was surprisingly good and though only slightly taller than her, led her masterfully round the floor. But his nearness gave her no thrill and when he rested his cheek against hers and sang part of the words of a love song in her ear, it was all she could do not to pull away from him. How irritating it was to be the recipient of an unwanted love.

It was after one o'clock before they returned to Holly Grove. The house was in darkness as he unlatched the front door and tenderly kissed her goodnight. His cheek was harder against hers than Carl's had been, though his lips were softer. She knew he was deliberately holding himself in check and once more felt ashamed at taking advantage of him.

'When may I see you?' he asked.

'I don't know. Carl will be in hospital from tomorrow and I'd like to be available in case he wants me.'

'I've an idea he'll be wanting Rosemary,' Duncan said flatly. 'But I'll leave you to make up your own mind. Just call me when you want me.'

'You're so sure Carl won't mind,' she said.

'Naturally I am. He told me so himself. And with Rosemary here, he'll be even more pleased to have you off his hands.'

With a squeeze of her arm he went back to his car, and despondently Laura closed the front door and walked across the hall. With her hand on the banisters she turned and went into the library. She switched on the lights and at once her eyes went to the settee. The cushions were smooth and only those on an armchair were rumpled. It looked as though Carl had remained in his wheelchair tonight and had not given Rosemary a chance to sit beside him. Poor Carl! He obviously did not want to disclose his feelings for the girl until he knew what the future held for him.

She turned off the lights and went upstairs. She was on the verge of going into her bedroom when she saw that the door of the sewing room at the end of the corridor was open. It was here that Mary washed her own clothes and ironed many of the things required by Carl. It was amazing the amount of linen he used. His skin chafed easily and any wrinkle in his clothes could cause acute discomfort. For this reason he changed frequently, and though his clothes were washed in a machine, Mary insisted on doing the ironing herself. This was what she was engaged in as Laura stepped into the warm atmosphere of the little workroom.

'Did you have a nice evening?' Mary asked.

'Duncan is always good company.'

'You do sound enthralled!'

'You know how I feel about him.'

'I know how your husband would like you to feel!'

'So do I.' Laura looked at her intently. 'Do you think the operation will be a success? I want you to be honest, Mary.'

'Dr Vanberg has an excellent reputation.'

'Is he so much better than Mr Edwards?'

'It isn't a question of being better. Dr Vanberg has pioneered a special technique in this type of operation.'

'Could Carl die if it went wrong?'

'Good lord, no!' Mary's answer was so spontaneous that Laura was instantly reassured.

'I want him to get better,' she said fiercely, 'even though it will mean the end of my life with him.'

'It isn't much of a life,' Mary replied. 'I think you'd be well shot of the whole affair. You're too young to waste your life pining for a man who hardly knows you exist—except as a sort of no man's land where he can hide!'

'He's preparing to cross the border into enemy territory,' Laura said wryly.

'Then why wait for him to tell you to go?'

Laura shrugged. 'You'll be free too, if the operation is successful. Will you go back to the hospital?'

'I might go to Australia with you. I think I've caught your travel bug.'

Laura tried, but failed, to be pleased at the prospect of having Mary as a companion on her travels. It would be harder to make a new life for herself if she was with someone who constantly reminded her of the old one. But to say this would be hurtful. Besides, she was not even sure she would go abroad. To run away from one's misery was not always the best way of conquering it; it might be better to stay and face it.

'What's up?' Mary asked. 'You look as if you've suddenly seen the light.'

Laura gave a vague reply, and though she remained chatting to Mary for a little while longer, she was glad to be finally alone in her bedroom to mull over this new thought. When had she subconsciously decided that running away would not solve her problem? And how much of this decision was due to Duncan and his obvious desire to marry her? Equally important, was she using Duncan as a sop to her pride, and could marrying him under these circumstances be a success?

The questions were incapable of being answered with any truth, and she vowed not to think of them again until she knew the result of Carl's operation. Yet if it was a failure, could she remain with him— even supposing that this was what he wanted? Here was another question she could not answer, at least not until she knew if Rosemary would remain in Carl's life if the operation did not succeed.

It was Rosemary herself who gave Laura the answer, for she came to the house at noon the next day, ostensibly to collect a compact which she had dropped from her handbag the evening before but mainly, Laura guessed, to find out what she could about Carl's relationship with the girl whom she still regarded as his secretary.

As always, Rosemary looked the picture of loveliness, with her big blue eyes, blonde hair and innocent expression. She dressed the part too, always wearing clothes of diaphanous material in pastel shades that enhanced her colouring. Though Laura was physically smaller, Rosemary had an ethereal quality that made her seem heavy and lumpy by comparison.

'I'm so glad we can talk to each other alone,' Rosemary breathed, putting her gold compact into her bag and perching lightly on the arm of a chair.

'I don't think we have anything to discuss,' Laura replied.

'I agree,' said Rosemary. 'What I have to say doesn't warrant a discussion.'

Laura's scalp prickled. It was not only the tone of Rosemary's voice that was different but also the phraseology, which was far less childish. Rosemary, it seemed, was not going to put on her baby act when they were alone together.

'I intend to marry Carl,' she announced.

'I doubt if you'll get him to commit bigamy,'

Laura said.

'I'm not joking, Laura. Carl realises he should never have married you. But you were always Miss Availability and——'

'I married Carl because he *asked* me to do so.'

'You mean because he wanted to escape from *me*,' Rosemary said. 'I know exactly why he turned to you and I know exactly why he's turning *away* from you. If you have any pride,' she continued viciously, 'you wouldn't wait for him to ask you to go.'

Laura clenched her hands. 'Carl knows he can have his freedom any time he wants.'

'He wants it now! Haven't you the sense to realise it? Why don't you just pack up and go?'

There was no answer to this and Laura wondered dismally why she should continue to suffer the indignity of living with a man who no longer wanted her.

'Carl is only having the operation because of me,' Rosemary said. 'That should show you how much he loves me.'

'I think he would like to walk for his own sake too,' Laura rasped, sickened by such manic egocentricity.

'But if I hadn't come back, he would never have considered it,' Rosemary persisted. 'You know that as well as I do.'

'All I know is that you walked out on him when he needed you most, and that you've only come back now because you can't find anyone richer!'

The round blue eyes grew rounder, giving Rosemary the look of a startled kitten. What a misnomer that was, Laura thought bitterly; vicious tiger was nearer the mark. Yet that was insulting a tiger, who had courage and pride, whereas Rosemary only

146

had greed.

'I'm not as hard up for a man as you,' the girl spat. 'I had a wonderful time in New York. You can ask your precious Duncan, if you don't believe me.'

'I'm sure you had a wonderful time. But if you'd had the chance of marrying a millionaire, you wouldn't have come back here!'

A flush tinged Rosemary's skin and against her will Laura realised she was not being fair to blame her entirely for what had happened. Carl was equally at fault, for he had welcomed her back into his life with open arms, his eagerness making it clear how much he regretted his marriage.

'What will you do if the operation fails?' Laura demanded. 'Will you run off and leave him again?'

'I won't make that mistake twice!'

'I can't see you spending your life with a man who's tied to a wheelchair.'

'He would still be a wonderful lover!' Rosemary said in a little-girl voice.

Laura almost gagged at the words. Blindly she turned her back on the room and stared out at the frost-tipped grass and leafless trees.

'You should leave Carl,' Rosemary said behind her. 'Get out before I tell him you're in love with him.'

With a gasp, Laura swung round. 'You wouldn't do that!'

'I would.'

With an effort Laura made herself look composed. 'If Carl thought I loved him, he'd feel so guilty about it, he'd never end our marriage. After all, I *did* help him when he needed me; and Carl has a great sense of responsibility.'

'So have you. You also have a conscience, and it wouldn't rest easy if you knew you were preventing him from being happy. So why don't you go quietly—while you still have your pride?'

'Because I care about Carl more than I care about my pride. I'm staying as long as I believe there's even the remotest chance of getting him to see you for what you are!'

Rosemary sauntered to the door. 'I'm not going to say "may the best girl win",' she drawled, 'because *I* am going to win!'

The door closed behind her and Laura sank on to the nearest chair. She tried to hold herself aloof from all Rosemary had said, but the words echoed around her with a lingering malevolence that infiltrated into her very bones. Rosemary was right in what she had said. Carl might feel responsible for having married her, but not so responsible that he had attempted to hide his regret for having done so. Knowing this she was foolish to go on staying here.

With a deep sigh she leaned back in the chair. What a strange mixture he was! On the one hand treating her as if she were an automaton and on the other hand displaying an almost frightening sensitivity to her feelings—as witnessed by the calculated way he had got rid of Mr Rogers. But it was these different facets that made Carl the man he was: clever and ruthless enough to succeed in business but charming and intuitive enough to do so without making too many enemies; virile and passionate enough to have a series of girl-friends, yet vulnerable enough to fall for a baby face and big blue eyes. Laura closed her own eyes and felt the trickle of tears squeeze between the lids. 'Am

I crying for Carl or myself?' she wondered and, with a deep sense of depression, knew she was crying for them both.

Later in the evening Laura went to see Carl. She had debated long and hard whether to do so, and had come to the conclusion that while she still bore his name, the least she could do was to carry on with the pretence that it meant something.

She dressed with unusual care for her visit, as if to show him that she had her own particular brand of charm. Most of her clothes were in the vivid colours he favoured, quite different from Rosemary's pastel ones, and she wondered if this was why he liked her to wear them: so that nothing about her reminded him of the girl he loved. She pushed the thought aside as she stepped into an emerald green silk dress and jacket. It was figure-fitting and made her realise she had lost a lot of weight. It emphasised the fullness of her breasts and also made her look taller. She was more heavy-handed than usual with her make-up, outlining her lips lavishly with scarlet and heavily coating her eyelashes so that they stuck out thick and straight. But warm brown eyes remained warm brown eyes no matter what one did to them, and no amount of willpower could give them the luminous quality of china blue ones. The thought made her brush her hair viciously. It was time she had it cut. It was curling well below her ears and was showing a tendency to curl forward along her temples. She looked far less the efficient young woman who had coped with Carl Anderson's business life and far more like a loved woman who was sharing his emotional one. A fat lot of sharing she had done with him. She clattered her brush down on the dressing table. Even when he had kissed her, it had only been a game of make-believe. He had never seen her in her own right, nor known her as she really was.

She drove with unusual ferocity to the hospital and was lucky not to be caught for speeding. But her spirit was less troubled by the time she went up in the lift to the corner room Carl occupied.

Surprisingly he was not in bed but sitting in an armchair by the window. The curtains were drawn behind him and a reading lamp flooded light on to his lap but left his face in shadow, making it impossible for her to read his expression.

'I thought you weren't coming to see me today,' he greeted her. 'If you had left it any later it wouldn't have been worth your while to come at all.'

He was always so much in command of himself that his irritation surprised her. 'I assumed you would be busy with a lot of tests,' she apologised.

'They finished at four o'clock. It's now eight.'

'If you'd wanted to see me earlier, you could have telephoned me.'

'Who said I wanted to see you?'

Convinced by now that something was wrong with him, she moved closer, but the darkness made it impossible for her to read anything in his face.

'Have you seen Mr Edwards today?' she asked.

'He's been in and out of here like a yo-yo.'

'You're obviously a favourite patient of his.'

'I'm the jam on his bread and butter!'

She ignored this. 'Will you be having more tests tomorrow?'

'I'll be having them every day until Dr Vanberg gets here on Friday.'

'When is he going to operate?' she asked.

'Monday, I suppose.'

Laura moistened her lips. 'Mary says he's pioneered a new technique.'

'He's a surgeon like any other,' Carl said irritably. 'Mary is inclined to go all starry-eyed at the thought of a man with a knife!'

Nothing could have been a less apt description of the blunt-spoken nurse, but Laura knew better than to contradict him. 'Even so, Dr Vanberg sounds interesting. I'd like to meet him.'

'I don't want you interfering in my private life.'

The cruelty of the remark stunned her. But it was so out of character for Carl to speak in this way that she was convinced something was seriously wrong. 'Obviously all the tests you've had have tired you,' she said calmly. 'It will be better if I leave you to rest.'

'Don't go yet.' He flung out his hands as though ashamed of his outburst. 'John Durban was here for a couple of hours. He probably tired me more than the tests.'

'You shouldn't be working while you're here,' she protested.

'Work relaxes me. Duncan was here too,' he added, 'but it was a private visit—not a business one. We talked about . . .' Carl's voice trailed away and when he resumed speaking, it was in different tone and about Rosemary, who had apparently come straight to see him after her visit to Holly Grove. 'She told me she'd been to the house to collect her compact,' he added, 'but I suspect the real reason was to talk to you.'

'It was.'

'I would prefer you not to see her again. You don't

like each other and I dislike the thought of you both bickering over me. It makes me feel like a bone caught between two dogs!'

'Bitches, you mean,' Laura said lightly. 'But I'm not partial to bones and I'm happy to let Rosemary have the pickings!'

'You know what I mean, Laura.' Carl shifted in his chair and the light fell across his face. It gave a shine to his skin and a glitter to his eyes, making them look like grey stones. 'I don't want you and Rosemary to settle my future for me.'

'I have no intention of settling your future. That rests with you.'

'As long as you realise it.'

'The big strong man who stands alone,' she said bitterly, and could immediately have kicked herself for her tactlessness. But Carl did not seem to mind and repeated her comment with a faint twist of humour.

'Until my accident, I never realised how important it was to stand alone. Nor did I appreciate how rarely one can do it. We're so often hedged round by other people's wishes.' His hands clenched on the blanket that covered his legs. 'I'm tired, Laura. I want to rest.'

She was at the door before she spoke. 'Do you want me to come and see you tomorrow? If I irritate you, it might be better if I didn't.'

There was a long silence before he answered. 'Perhaps it *would* be better. I'm sorry, Laura.'

'You don't need to be,' she said huskily, and wished with all her heart that she had never agreed to marry him. At least it would not have put him in a position which he found embarrassing and painful. Should she tell him she would leave him or should she wait for him to ask her to go? If the other girl in his life was not Rosemary, she would have had no hesitation in leaving immediately, but as long as he was still trying to fight his love, she would remain to help him.

'Let me know when you want to see me, Carl,' she said quietly. 'I'll be at home.'

CHAPTER THIRTEEN

THINKING about Carl's display of temper, Laura knew that only emotional stress could have caused it. She tried to see something positive in it, but all she saw was that he knew her well enough not to pretend with her and liked her little enough not to care if he hurt her.

Obeying his wishes, she did not go to the hospital the next day and, like a ghost, wandered around the house, unable to settle anywhere for long. Finally her restlessness drove her to the kitchen where, despite the disapproval of the cook, she set about baking cakes she did not want to eat, ignoring the aid of the electric mixer and venting her unrest upon the hapless batter. Later, tired but triumphant, she carried a fragrant plateful of buns to the drawing room and was sampling her work when Duncan arrived. It was so unusual for him to call uninvited that she looked at him apprehensively, afraid that he was bringing bad news.

'There's nothing wrong,' he assured her in answer to her question, 'Stop looking worried.' He took her hand and drew her close, then gave her a look of surprise. 'You smell of baking!'

'Which isn't surprising, since I've just made some cakes.' She pointed to the table behind her. 'José is bringing in some coffee, so I'll expect you to sample my culinary efforts.'

'I never knew you could cook as well.'

'As well as most women,' she smiled.

'As well as being beautiful, intelligent and highly efficient,' he amended.

His admiration was what she needed and she gave him a warm smile. She might profess to be unhurt by Carl's temper, but in her heart she knew she was bruised from it.

'Have you seen Carl today?' she asked, sitting down by the fire.

'I've just come from the hospital. He's in fairly good spirits, considering.'

She pondered Duncan's use of the word 'considering', not sure if he was relating it to the painful tests Carl was undergoing. She gave him a measured look and saw something in his expression that disquieted her. 'Considering what, Duncan?'

'Considering the risk he's taking.'

The fear that had lain dormant in her since she had learned of Carl's operation sprang into life. 'So it *is* dangerous? I suspected, but I wasn't sure.'

'It is extremely dangerous.'

'I asked Mary about it, but ...' Laura stopped, remembering how evasive Mary's answer had been. Under normal circumstances she would have probed further, but Rosemary's all-pervading presence had made her so rattled that she had not done anything about it. 'Exactly how dangerous is it?' she demanded.

There was a slight pause. 'He won't die from it, if it went wrong but—but it has far less than a fifty-fifty chance of going right. Dr Vanberg is the pioneer of this particular technique, as you know, but he hasn't performed all that many operations that have required it. Maybe fifty.'

'And of those fifty, how many were able to walk again?'

'Twelve.'

The arrival of José with the coffee prevented Laura from replying and she waited until the butler had left the room before she did so. 'That isn't a very good percentage, is it, Duncan?'

'No,' he said frankly. 'And if I were in Carl's place, I would never consider taking it.'

The words gave additional bitterness to thoughts which Laura already found galling. It seemed no risk was too great for Carl to take in order to be a whole man for Rosemary.

'I'm not sure I'd be prepared to take the risk even for you,' Duncan continued. 'I would like to think that if a woman loved me, she'd prefer me to be in a wheelchair than see me flat on my back like a log of wood—given that the operation failed, of course.'

Laura stared stared at him in perplexity. 'A log of wood? Are you saying that if the operation failed, Carl won't remain the way he is now?'

'That's exactly what I'm saying.' Duncan rose and paced the floor. 'I've known for days that the operation was dangerous, but it wasn't until this morning—when I bumped into Mr Edwards—that I learned exactly what it entailed. If the operation fails, Carl will look back on the manoeuvrability he had when he was in his wheelchair the way a man dying of thirst looks at water!'

The coffee pot Laura was holding shook so violently that she set it down. 'He mustn't be allowed to do it! We've got to stop him, Duncan.'

'Do you think I haven't tried? I've been with him for the past hour—it's why I'm here now. Carl will be furious with me for telling you, but I felt you had to know. Maybe *you* can get him to see sense.'

'He won't listen to me,' Laura said bitterly. 'Rosemary is the only one who can stop him.' She stood up. 'I must go and see her.'

'She arrived at the hospital as I left,' Duncan said. 'You can't talk to her in front of Carl.'

'I'll wait outside for her,' Laura replied. 'She's got to stop Carl from going through with this.'

'I'll come with you,' said Duncan.

Gratefully Laura accepted the offer and, pausing only to put on a coat, went with him to his car. The rush-hour traffic was already clogging the roads like heavy mud in a river and they moved sluggishly southwards. Neither of them made any conversation, both too concerned over Carl to bother with small talk. How deeply Carl must love Rosemary if he could take such an appalling risk to get her! Until now, Laura had seen his need for the girl as a physical one, but now she saw it as an obsession that made it impossible for him to think rationally. To run the risk of an operation that could leave him totally immobile! He was out of his mind to consider it. Yet he was going to do it; he was deliberately betting on odds that even a gambler would eschew: and all because of Rosemary.

They reached the hospital and Duncan parked the car and elected to stay in it.

'It will be better if you talk to Rosemary by yourself,' he explained. 'But if you need me, I'll be here.'

Tensely Laura went up to the waiting room on Carl's floor. Keeping the door ajar, she placed her chair where it gave her a view of the lifts, in order not to miss Rosemary when she came out of Carl's

157

room. Carefully she tried to work out exactly what she would say to Rosemary. But there was no way of gently leading up to it. The truth was too ugly to be disguised.

A flash of silver grey mink brought her to her feet and she called Rosemary's name. The girl swung round from the lift door, surprise on her face as she saw who it was.

'Carl's too tired to see anyone else,' she said in a triumphant voice, 'particularly *you*.'

'I haven't come to see Carl,' Laura replied. 'I came to talk to you.'

'What about?'

'Come in here and I'll tell you.'

Mystified by Laura's tone, Rosemary did as she was told, and in terse sentences Laura told her all she had learned from Duncan. Because the truth was dramatic enough, she did not embellish it further. Only when it came to describing the life Carl would face if the operation failed—as it had done in the vast majority of cases—did her control slip and her voice become almost inaudible.

'You can't let him go ahead with it,' she concluded. 'You are the only person who can make him change his mind.'

'At least you have enough sense to know *you* can't,' Rosemary retorted, and then lapsed into silence.

Laura watched the lovely face, seeing a myriad expressions pass over it, none of which she could identify. Was it fear, love, hope, anguish? She clasped her hands tightly and waited for the girl to speak.

'I don't see why I should tell Carl what to do,' Rosemary said at last, her voice cool as spring water.

'After all, it's his life and if he doesn't want to live it in a wheelchair, who can blame him?'

'Do you think he'll want to live it flat on his back?'

'Why be pessimistic? He might be completely cured.'

'I've just told you the risk,' Laura cried.

'It's still Carl's choice.'

'He's doing it for *you*. How will you feel if the operation fails? You'll never forgive yourself.'

'I would still marry him,' Rosemary said, and looked oddly satisfied. 'It wouldn't be a real marriage—the way it could be now—but I wouldn't leave him, you know. I would just—I would have to make a life for myself.'

Laura's skin prickled as though a thousand insects were crawling over it. With a clarity that could not be denied she saw the reasoning behind Rosemary's statement.

'You don't mind if Carl is paralysed!' she gasped. 'Then you could be his wife without any obligation. I knew you never loved him,' she continued bitterly, 'but I never realised you hated him!'

'Don't be so dramatic!'

'It's true. If you had any decent human feelings for him, you'd never let him take such a risk. But you aren't capable of feeling anything for anyone except yourself. You're a heartless, calculating bitch!'

'Carl loves me and I'm going to marry him as soon as he's free of you!' Rosemary smoothed the fur of her coat, preening herself in it like a satisfied animal. 'I happen to think that the risk he's taking is worthwhile.'

'*You* have nothing to lose!'

'But Carl has a great deal to gain. And that's what matters to him,' Rosemary said triumphantly.

'You've got to stop him,' Laura persisted, hoping that Rosemary's callous attitude came from lack of imagination and not lack of heart. 'The risk is too high. You can't let him take it.'

'I can and I will!' Rosemary said in her sweetest voice. 'Why don't you mind your own business and keep out of my way? Your intensity bores me!'

In a flurry of mink she disappeared, leaving Laura with one last option open to her. She hated having to take it, but she had no choice. Taking several deep breaths, she went along the corridor to Carl's room.

Bracing herself for a cool reception, she was surprised by his reaction to her entrance, for he paled visibly. It showed up unexpected lines on his face that that not been there before his accident, and her heart turned over at the sight of them. But she must steel herself for what she had to say; steel herself for the way he would react to it.

'I know you told me not to come here until you asked me,' she began breathlessly, 'but Duncan came to see me this afternoon and told me the truth about your operation.'

'I see.' The words held no meaning. They were just said and hung lifeless in the air like washing on a line.

'You can't have the operation,' she said clearly. 'It's madness. I won't let you do it!'

'You can't stop me.' Again the words were spoken without expression but, looking into his face, she saw the bleakness in his eyes.

'You might become totally paralysed. Have you thought what your life would be if that happened?'

'All I can think of is what my life is like now.'

'At least you can get round in a wheelchair. You can't walk, but you can do a lot of other things for yourself. You aren't helpless—which you *will* be if this operation fails.'

'It's my life, and I'm willing to take the risk.'

'You aren't risking your life, you're risking your sanity! You'll go crazy if you wake up from the anaesthetic and find you can't move a single muscle!' She saw his eyelids flicker and knew she dared not stop now. She had to make him see what the future might hold for him; not that she needed to exaggerate, for the truth was dreadful enough. 'You'd be a helpless log lying in bed twenty-four hours out of twenty-four. You would need someone to feed you, wash you, wipe your mouth when you drink a cup of tea, help you to——'

'Stop it!' he shouted, and gave such a violent jerk in the bed that the castors moved. 'I don't need you to tell me what might happen. I've thought about nothing else for weeks! But I'm going to have it done. It's a risk I've got to take.'

'A risk for what?' she choked. 'So that you can marry Rosemary? You aren't just a cripple, Carl, you're blind as well!'

'I don't want to talk about it.' His voice was barely audible, but his hands, gripping the sheet till the knuckles went white, gave him away. 'Duncan had no right to tell you the truth. I spoke to him in confidence.'

'You didn't talk to him as a lawyer,' she cried, 'but as a friend. That's why he told me.'

'Then he's wasted his time. My mind is made up. Now please go. I can't take any more scenes.'

He turned his face into the pillow and she stared

161

at the back of his head, seeing the thick hair lying against the nape of his neck and longing to rest her cheek against it. But she had no right to do so and slowly she backed to the door.

'Very well, Carl, I'll go. But I still think you're a fool.'

Her hand was on the knob when he spoke again. 'Aren't you going to wish me luck?'

She did not turn to look at him. 'Of course I wish you luck. You'll need every bit of it.' She fumbled at the handle, but because her hands were clammy, she could not grip it.

'Try to understand why I'm doing it,' he said huskily. 'I won't let myself be a burden on the woman I love. I've got to be a whole man.'

At this she swung round, eyes blazing. 'Even in in a wheelchair you're more of a man than anyone I've known! If you don't know that for yourself . . .'

She wrenched at the door again. This time it opened and she sped down the corridor. She would never see Carl again. With all her heart she prayed that the risk he was taking would pay off. Yet even if he became well, he would not be happy with Rosemary. One day he would discover what she was. No, that was a stupid thing to say. He already knew what she was and he didn't care.

'Oh, Carl,' she whispered, 'how can you be such a fool?'

By the time she reached Duncan she was dry-eyed and in control of herself.

'I saw Rosemary leave the hospital,' he commented. 'As you didn't come out with her, I assumed you went to see Carl?'

'Yes. Rosemary wouldn't go herself. She says if Carl wants to take the risk, it's his affair.'

'I thought she might say that.'

'Did you?'

He nodded. 'You don't know as much about human behaviour as I do. Nothing people do can surprise me.'

'She can't even like him,' Laura whispered. 'If she had any normal feelings, she ... But Carl doesn't care. He doesn't even see it.'

'Because he doesn't want to. Try not to be too upset about Carl. We've both tried to make him see the consequences and we can't do more than that. In the final event, it's *his* life and he must be allowed to make his own decision how he wants to live it. All we can do is to be there if he should need us.'

'Whatever the outcome of the operation, he won't need me,' Laura said. 'Rosemary will marry him no matter what.'

'That's all to the good. You'll be better off if you put him from your mind.' Duncan slid across the seat until he was close beside her. 'Don't tell me this isn't the time or place to talk of our future, because if I listen to you, there never will be the right time and place. I love you and I want to marry you. You've allowed your loyalty to Carl to affect your whole life, and you've got to stop thinking about him. We've done as much as we can and it isn't our business to do more. Besides, he would hate us for it if we did.'

'He already hates me,' Laura said. 'He made that clear yesterday and even clearer today. He isn't the same man I worked for all these years,' she burst out. 'Meeting Rosemary has changed his entire life. It was the reason for his accident. He was trying to get so much done before he went on his honeymoon.'

'You can't blame him for that,' Duncan protested.

'I do! He wasn't just trying to put the business in order—he was staying up till all hours in nightclubs and restaurants, running after Rosemary as if he didn't have a mind of his own. I hate him for it,' she cried. 'He doesn't deserve us to worry about him!'

'You know you don't mean that.' Duncan pulled her into his arms and, because she knew he was right, she lapsed into silence.

'Marry me,' Duncan begged. 'Marry me and come to New York.'

'Very well,' she said, without thinking. 'I'd like to go to New York.'

For an instant he was motionless, then he pushed her away and stared into her face. 'You will?' he said jubilantly. 'I can't believe it!'

Staring back at him, Laura could not believe it either. What on earth had made her say yes? How could she marry Duncan when she was Carl's wife? But Carl did not want her. In a few months their marriage would be annulled and Rosemary would become his wife. She bit her lip hard to stop herself crying out. If Carl became well and strong again, then jealousy would consume her like a fire, and if he were doomed to lie paralysed, then hatred for Rosemary would consume her with even greater intensity, no matter where she lived or what other job she took.

Perhaps the best solution was to become Duncan's wife. A happy marriage had grown from far less auspicious beginnings.

'How do I get my freedom?' she asked.

'Leave it to me. I'll talk to Carl and——'

'Not yet,' she interrupted. 'Wait until after the operation.'

'I don't see why. He'll be pleased to know you're going to be happy.'

'There won't be any publicity, will there?'

'Not if it's done carefully. The publicity will come when he marries Rosemary.'

Duncan could not have said anything more calculated to stiffen Laura's wavering doubts. 'How soon will I be free?' she asked.

'A couple of months. I'll do my best to expedite it.' He put his hand under her chin and tilted up her face. 'I want to make you my wife as soon as I can. I'm Carl's age and I've waited long enough before taking the plunge.' He pressed his lips to hers and, fired by her nearness, his arms came round her with unexpected strength. 'I love you,' he muttered.

Laura tried to respond to his kisses. But though she forced her body to relax, her mind remained aloof and critical. She was aware of Duncan's quickened breathing, of his seeking hands that touched her without arousing her, and she wanted to push him away and tell him it was all a mistake. But though the words screamed inside her, she remained mute, knowing only immeasurable relief when he finally released her and moved back to sit behind the wheel.

'We'll be very happy together, my darling,' he said. 'At the moment you're still upset at what might happen to Carl, but once the operation is over and we're in New York, you'll feel a different person.'

He went on talking about the life they would

165

lead, and though she did not take in a word he said, she must have made the right responses, for he did not notice her silence and looked singularly content when he finally deposited her at Holly Grove.

'We'll go out tomorrow and celebrate our engagement,' he murmured, kissing her hand. 'I want to buy you a ring, but the lawyer in me won't let me! I will have to wait until you're legally free before I do that.'

She glanced at the ruby on her finger. It glowed like blood—Carl's blood—and she shivered and drew her hand away from his. 'I don't want an engagement ring, Duncan.'

'Then we'll wait until I buy you a wedding ring.'

His hold became more possessive, but she pulled away from him and put her hands to her temples as if she had a headache. Instantly he apologised for not seeing how pale she was, which made her feel more guilty. How easily a man could be fooled by the woman he loved!

There was not so much difference between Rosemary and herself, she thought bleakly as she finally closed the door on Duncan and went up to her room. They would each be marrying a man they did not love, though for quite different reasons.

CHAPTER FOURTEEN

DUNCAN telephoned Laura the following afternoon to say he would be kept late at the office but would send a car to collect her.

'Forgive me for not coming for you myself,' he apologised, 'but if I can put in another hour at my desk, I'll be able to consign a huge bundle of files to limbo for another year.'

'Would you prefer to call off our dinner?'

'Certainly not. I'm looking forward to it.'

'Don't bother sending a car for me,' she assured him. 'I'll get a taxi.' She hesitated. 'Have you seen Carl today?'

'Yes. I'll tell you about it later.'

She wondered if he was being discreet because there was someone in the office or because what he had to say was unpalatable, and she was apprehensive when she walked into the Dorchester bar where they had arranged to meet. Duncan was at a corner table, a bottle of champagne and two glasses in front of him. The sight of his smiling face reawakened the doubts she had been wrestling with, and though she regretted having to destroy his happiness, she could not continue with this falsehood.

'You look lovely, darling,' he said. 'That pink thing suits you.'

'This pink thing is the most expensive dress I own!'

'Will you want a white wedding?' he asked suddenly. 'That's one thing we haven't discussed.'

Laura's heart thumped loudly and though she saw Duncan's lips moving, she could not hear a word he said. But after a few seconds the pounding lessened and she was able to follow him without giving away the shock his words had caused.

'Can't we wait until I'm free before we talk about marriage?' she asked.

'Your marriage to Carl is meaningless.'

'It's still legal.'

'Not for long. And I refuse to let you have a guilt complex about what you're doing. You helped Carl when he needed it, but he doesn't need your help any more. As a matter of fact he's delighted at our news. I told him about us this morning.'

Champagne splashed over the rim of Laura's glass on to her fingers and Duncan took the glass from her and set it on the table.

'Carl couldn't have been more pleased at the news,' he reiterated. 'So stop looking gloomy.'

For the life of her Laura could not speak. She stared at the table and then at her hands; anywhere as long as it wasn't into Duncan's happy face.

'Think of the future, darling.' He was speaking again. 'A few months from now and we'll be living a completely different life.'

With Carl living his own life, Laura thought bleakly. Either vigorous as before or helplessly dependent. But whichever way it was, it would be a life shared with Rosemary.

'Did Carl want to see me?' she asked, bending to pick up her glass so the fall of her hair would hide her face.

'He doesn't want to see anybody. He's in an odd frame of mind. I didn't notice it much when I saw him this morning, but when I went back this afternoon——'

'You've seen him twice today?' she interrupted.

'Yes. He had to sign some more papers. The Company is going from strength to strength. It amazes me how he manages to hold everything together. If this operation fails, he won't be able to go on doing it.'

'Don't,' she begged. 'I can't bear to think of it.'

Yet think of it she did for the rest of the evening and during the next interminable day. Never had time passed so slowly and each time she looked at her watch she thought it had stopped. But eventually the evening arrived and Duncan with it, carrying an extravagant bouquet of flowers. He wore a light grey suit instead of his usual dark one and he looked much more carefree, though his manner was still controlled.

'I thought we would have a quiet evening,' he said. 'We can either dine locally or——' he hesitated, 'I would be happy to stay here and have a snack.'

'With our high-priced chef in the kitchen, we can rustle up more than a snack,' she said drily. 'It's fantastic how much this house costs Carl to run.'

'He's earned his luxuries,' said Duncan. 'Though I don't think he'd miss them if he didn't have them. Sometimes I feel he's still a lumberjack at heart.'

'A man of all trades,' she said with a tight smile.

'Unlike me,' he chuckled. 'I could never be anything other than a lawyer.'

'You would have made a good doctor.'

'Despite an annoying tendency to go green at the sight of blood?'

She laughed. 'You have an excellent bedside manner.'

'Wait till you see it in action!'

Afraid he was going to pull her into his arms, she went over to the tray of drinks and poured him a whisky, adding the right amount of soda and remembering to put in ice, which was a habit he had acquired during his stay in New York.

They dined in the breakfast room, preferring it to the large dining room which would have over-powered them. The outside lights had been switched on and the pool glowed blue beneath the starlit sky. Would Carl ever swim in those waters again? she wondered, and hastily concentrated on her lobster soufflé. How well she remembered the first time she had seen Carl swim after his accident. She had gone to Hampstead High Street to buy him some books and had returned to hear laughter coming from the garden. Curious to know who could be out on a cold January day, she had been astonished to see steam rising from the pool and, in the middle of it, Carl swimming vigorously. For a wild, delirious moment she had thought he had regained the use of his legs, until she had realised he was only using his arms, his shoulder muscles bulging as he ploughed his way through the water.

'Laura, come back!'

With a start she saw that Duncan was looking at her. 'You were a million miles away from me,' he accused. 'I hope you were thinking of our future?'

It was impossible to lie to him. 'I was thinking of Carl. I won't be able to get him out of my mind until after the operation. I daren't let myself think

170

beyond that point.'

'We'll know the worst in about twenty-four hours,' he said quietly.

Her fork slipped from her shaking hand. 'You mean it's being done tomorrow?'

'Yes. Dr Vanberg arrived tonight and the operation has been brought forward at Carl's insistence. I gather he's refused to have any more tests. He says he wants it done now.'

'He's mad,' she shivered.

'He's reached the end of his tether,' Duncan corrected. 'A man can take so much and no more.'

'Does Rosemary know?'

'I assume so. I didn't see her at the hospital, thank goodness. Like you, it would be all I could do to talk to her civilly.'

'I wouldn't talk to her at all,' Laura said.

'You have no need. You don't even have to see Carl if you don't wish. I mean if the news is bad.'

'I can't bear to think of it,' she cried, and pushed away her plate.

'I wish I'd kept quiet about the operation,' he muttered. 'I didn't intend to tell you until it was over.'

'I'm glad you told me.'

'So that you can sit and worry your heart out?'

'What time are they doing it?' she asked.

'First thing in the morning,' he said reluctantly. 'But it's a long operation. Five or six hours at least. Mr Edwards was telling me what they have to do.'

'I don't want to know,' Laura shuddered. 'All I'm concerned with is the result.'

'Right now I'm concerned over you,' Duncan complained. 'Do eat up, darling, you're far too thin.'

With an effort Laura tried to do as he ordered. Her throat was tight with unshed tears and she tried to swallow her food without chewing it; it was better to risk indigestion than have Duncan go on looking at her with such solicitude. She was immeasurably relieved when the meal finally came to an end and they returned to the drawing room for coffee.

Luckily there was an interesting documentary on the television which occupied his time and enabled her to sit beside him without having to make conversation. She prayed he would not try to make love to her, fearing that if he did, she might have hysterics. Fortunately he sensed her mood, for though he held her hand he made no other attempt at intimacy and even his goodnight kiss was brief.

'Will you be going to the hospital?' she asked as he reached his car.

'I told Mr Edwards I would get there about eleven.'

'When will they know the result?'

'Not for a couple of days.'

With Duncan gone, Laura wandered around the downstairs rooms. She was too overwrought to sleep, nor did she want to go to bed. How heavily the time was going to drag for the next few days. If only she could take a pill and wake up when it was all over. Fleetingly she thought of Rosemary and knew that wherever the girl was, she was giving little thought to the man lying in his narrow hospital bed. What were Carl's thoughts at this precise moment? Did he regret the choice he had made or was he still as adamant as he had been when she had last seen him? She could not believe he was unafraid and wished with all her heart that she had the right to comfort him. But she would only have had that right if he had loved her and, had he done so, she would never have allowed him to take this dreadful risk.

Unaware of what she was doing, she went into the garden. The air was cold, but she did not return to the house for her coat. Slowly she walked round the pool, staring into its blue depths and seeing Carl's silver blond hair in the water, his strong arms cleaving through it and sending up the spray.

At noon the following day Duncan rang. He had no news and merely told her the operation was still in progress. At two o'clock he called again to say that Carl had been taken to the intensive care unit where he was being watched over by an electronic nurse who would monitor his pulse beat, heart rate and blood pressure.

'When will we know if . . .' She could not go on.

'In about forty-eight hours,' Duncan said. 'Now put down the phone and go and have something to eat before you faint from lack of food.'

'How do you know I haven't eaten?'

'One doesn't need to be psychic to know the obvious,' he said grimly. 'Promise me you'll have some coffee and toast or I'll come up and force-feed you!'

Shakily she promised to do as he ordered and went to the kitchen where the staff were waiting to hear the news of Carl's operation. The house was sombre with expectancy, yet she loved it as much in this mood as she did in all its other ones. It was a house meant for happy people and children's voices. But children's voices were one thing it might never know unless Carl and Rosemary adopted some.

Angry at her pessimism, Laura forced herself to think the exact opposite. The operation would be a success and Carl would soon be living life to the full, the way he had always lived it. But this time Rosemary would be beside him: the girl with china blue eyes and no heart.

To Laura's relief, Duncan did not come to the house that night, grumbling that an unexpected business engagement would keep him in town until ten o'clock. She knew that, given the word, he would drive over to see her afterwards, and firmly told him she intended to have an early night and would see him the following day.

She went to bed not expecting to sleep, but the wakeful hours of the night before had taken their toll and, the moment her head touched the pillow, she knew no more until she awoke to find the sun streaming through her windows. At once she sat up and dialled the hospital, fearful that something had happened to Carl while she had been asleep.

'He awoke for a moment last night,' the Sister told her, 'but Dr Vanberg has been in several times to see him and is coming back in an hour. If you care to come down, he'll be able to tell you if the operation was successful.'

'I was told we wouldn't know for forty-eight hours,' Laura gasped.

The Sister gave a non-committal murmur and Laura put down the receiver and jumped out of bed. It was wrong of Duncan to lie to her. He should have given her the chance of being at the hospital when the final truth was known.

Agitatedly she bathed and dressed, then ran down the hall, still undecided what to do. She longed to go to the hospital yet could not face the prospect of seeing Rosemary. If the news was bad, she would want to get her hands round that slender throat and squeeze it until there was no more life left. Horrified at where her thoughts were taking her, she walked from room to room and was in Carl's study when Duncan came through the door.

The blood drained from her head and she held out her hands to him.

He caught them tightly. 'It's all right, Laura. It was a success! In a fortnight Carl will be up and about again and in a month he'll be walking.'

Duncan's voice receded into an indistinct murmur and the ground rocked beneath her as she sank down on it.

When she recovered her senses it was to find herself lying on the settee in the drawing room. There was a taste of brandy in her mouth and the hard rim of a glass pressing on her lips. She pushed it away and sat up. Duncan straightened and set the glass on the table. He looked grave and for a moment Laura was afraid she had misheard him.

'You didn't lie about Carl, did you?' she cried.

'No, he's fine. It's you I'm worried about.'

'There's no need,' she said shakily. 'I suppose one slice of toast isn't enough to keep me going for twenty-four hours.'

'For heaven's sake!' he said violently and, striding over to the wall, gave the bell a firm push.

A quarter of an hour later, at his command, José wheeled in a trolley. On it were coffee and sandwiches and an omelette for herself.

'Not a word from you until you've eaten it,' Duncan ordered, and refused to speak again until her plate was empty. Only then did he relax and smile. 'Now I'll answer all your questions.'

'There's only one. Will Carl be completely well?'

'A hundred per cent. They'll be moving him back to his own room tonight and he'll be allowed visitors tomorrow. Rosemary was already there when I left,' he added drily. 'So you see her gamble paid off.'

'Carl's gamble,' Laura retorted, and burst into tears.

Instantly Duncan was beside her, cradling her in his arms. His shoulder was hard and bony, not broad and firm the way Carl's had been the night she had lain close to him on this self-same settee.

'He deserves someone better than Rosemary,' she sobbed. 'It isn't fair.'

'It's what he wants,' Duncan pacified. 'He'll be happy with her.'

'No, he won't. She'll break his heart and make a fool of him.'

'At least he'll be able to walk away from her when she does.'

This only made Laura cry harder and Duncan finally lapsed into silence and waited for the tears to cease of their own accord. It was only the re-entry of José with fresh coffee that forced Laura to some semblance of control, and she patted her face in-effectually with her handkerchief.

'I'm sorry for making such a fool of myself,' she hiccoughed.

'There's no need to apologise.' Duncan gave a faint smile. 'You've been living on your nerves since you knew the risk of the operation.' He poured more coffee for them both. 'When will you go and see Carl?'

'I'm not.'

'He'll be expecting you.'

'He has Rosemary; he doesn't need anyone else.'

'And you have me,' Duncan said, 'so *you* don't need anyone else.'

There was an odd note in his voice which made her hands shake. Her cup rattled in its saucer and she set it down on the tray.

'It isn't only Carl who's blind,' Duncan went on. 'I am too. Why didn't you tell me the truth, Laura? Didn't you know it yourself, or were you ashamed to admit it?'

Silently she stared at him and he put his hands on her shoulders and gave her a gentle shake. 'You love Carl, don't you? If I hadn't been so much in love with you myself, I would have realised it weeks ago. You wouldn't have married him otherwise, nor would you have been so hurt by Rosemary.' His voice quickened. 'And of course it explains her vindictiveness to *you*. She knows you love Carl too. It's only Carl who doesn't know it.'

'He must *never* know,' Laura said, realising it was impossible to prevaricate any longer. 'I should never have agreed to marry you, Duncan. If I'd been more in control of myself the other night, I wouldn't have let you talk me into it.'

'I did rather force your hand,' he said wryly. 'But I won't hold you to your promise.'

It was typical of Duncan to say this, and she wished with all her heart that she could agree to marry him. But he deserved something far more than second best, which was all she would ever be able to give any man other than Carl.

'Don't search for kind words,' he continued. 'Nothing will compensate me for losing you.'

'I wish it could have been different,' she cried.

'So do I.' He moved over to the fireplace, thin and sober in his dark suit. 'This doesn't change anything for Carl and Rosemary, you know.'

'I realise that.'

'What will you do?' he asked.

'What I was going to do in the beginning, I suppose. Get a job abroad.' Still joyous with the knowledge that Carl was going to be well, she was in no mood to think clearly. 'It doesn't matter where I go,' she said vaguely, 'as long as it's far from England.'

'I have an aunt in Brazil who's looking for a companion,' Duncan said unexpectedly. 'If you're interested, I can call her for you.'

'Would you?' She went towards him and then stopped. But he held out his hand and she took it, liking him so much at this moment that had he asked her to change her mind and marry him, she would have agreed.

'It wouldn't work, darling,' he said, as if guessing her thoughts. 'Not yet, anyway. Carl is still too close to you and I'm still too aware of it. But go to Brazil. At least I'll know where you are and how I can get in touch with you. Perhaps one day we can start again.'

She nodded and drew his hand to her cheek. 'Dear Duncan, I hope you get what you deserve.'

'That's up to you,' he said whimsically and, to lighten the mood, used his free hand to give her hair a tweak. 'I'll call Rio and tell my aunt you're on your way.'

CHAPTER FIFTEEN

LAURA tossed back her hair and quickened her pace, defying the black-haired Brazilian who had been following her along the promenade for the past ten minutes to come any closer. The one thing she had learned in her six weeks here was that to give a Brazilian male a millimetre would immediately encourage him to take a mile.

'Excuse me,' the young man said, breathing heavily in her ear.

'I'll do nothing of the sort,' Laura snapped, and swung round on him, handbag raised. 'If you don't stop following me, I'll scream!'

The man hesitated and she drew a deep breath and opened her mouth. With a quick bow, he melted into the shade of a building, leaving her to continue her walk unimpeded.

She had been aware of him following her since she had left the apartment that overlooked the fashionable Copacabana beach. But then it had been unwise of her to go for a walk alone; Mrs Richards was always telling her this. Still, Mrs Richards had a highly nervous disposition and was even reluctant to sit out alone on the balcony where she lived. Laura smiled at the memory of some of the old lady's foibles but knew that, despite them, she was lucky to be working in this exotic land. Mrs Richards was equally pleased to have her, particularly since she was aware of her nephew's friendship for her.

'I gather Duncan is fond of you,' she had said a few days ago. 'You are the first girl I have known him to bother about and certainly the only one he has ever recommended to me. But if you don't love him, don't let him corral you into marriage.'

'Corral me?' Laura had echoed.

'It's what they do to horses, and some men have a tendency to liken their womenfolk to fillies! Duncan in particular is inclined to think that way. He won't try and rope you in, though. He's too subtle. He believes that if he keeps a gentle hand on the bridle, you'll soon start nuzzling for his particular piece of sugar!'

Laura had burst out laughing and had assured the old lady that much as she liked Duncan, she had reached the stage where marriage could only be contemplated if love came with it. 'And I'm afraid I don't love him,' she had said. 'I left England because——'

'I know why,' Mrs Richards had interrupted. 'Don't upset yourself by talking of it. I'm only glad Mr Anderson has recovered the use of his legs. He's going to be led a pretty dance by his particular little filly.'

Laura remembered this as she strolled along the uneven pavement that bordered the wide sandy beaches of this tropical city. She had only heard once from Duncan since she had arrived here, and that had been a week after leaving London. Since then there had been no word from him and she wondered if he was deliberately keeping silent in the hope it might encourage her to miss him. Unfortunately it was having the opposite effect, for he was becoming a dimmer memory. If only the same thing could happen to Carl! Even without thinking of him she found him taking over her thoughts. He seemed to be entwined into the very roots of her being.

She sighed and came to a halt. It was the best time of the year to be in Rio, but even so it was extremely hot and the bodice of her yellow silk dress clung to her. She had gained the weight she had lost and her pale skin was tanned by the fierce sun. To a casual observer she was a brown-haired, girl, though a more astute eye would have seen the sad droop to the gentle mouth and the violet shadows beneath the warm brown eyes. She started to walk again, not sure whether to continue along the front or take one of the side turnings and look at a few of the boutiques. But the shimmering blue sea tempted her to remain where she was, and she continued her stroll around the bay, wishing that the planners who had built the opulent hotels that rose on her left had thought to keep some of the luxurious vegetation and not cover it all with concrete.

There was another monstrous concrete pile being put up some twenty yards ahead of her; a hotel, possibly, or an apartment block. Head on one side, she regarded it and, as she did so, became intrigued by its shape, which was far more elegant than the buildings either side of it. Mindful of the traffic— for it had an alarming tendency to speed up when there was a pedestrian on the road—she crossed to the other side to get a better look at it.

There were several signboards in the front and her pulse jumped as she saw the name Anderson. This was one of Carl's projects! She could not remember them quoting for a contract in Rio and supposed it had been done after she had left the company. She moved closer to peer in at the ground floor. Yes, it was going to be an apartment house, and an exceptionally luxurious one. It was the type of work which Carl had always regarded as 'gravy' and which he generally gave to one of the other directors to supervise—once he himself had approved all the plans. Thinking of him in relation to his work made her wonder what he was doing now. Their marriage had not yet been annulled, though this would not stop him from living with Rosemary. He had so much time to make up for, so much loving to do. She gave a gasp of pain and put her hand on a signboard to steady herself.

'It isn't good to stand in the sun too long,' a soft voice said behind her. 'It's the best way of getting sunstroke.'

Laura remained rooted to the spot. 'I knew it,' she thought wildly. 'I knew that if I didn't stop thinking of Carl, I would go crazy.'

'Aren't you going to turn and say hello to me?' the soft voice continued and, as she still remained motionless, strong hands reached out and swung her round.

No, she wasn't crazy. It really was Carl standing in front of her. But a Carl she had never thought to see again. Tall, broad-shouldered, fair hair glinting in the sunlight, eyes startlingly grey in a face that was tanned and smiling.

'Hello, Carl,' she said lamely. 'How—how nice to see you.'

'How nice to see you too,' he said gravely and, catching her elbow in a grip that made her wince, propelled her at breakneck speed towards the lush entrance of one of the newest hotels.

'How long have you been here?' she said in an attempt to bring rationality into what she still thought to be a dream. 'And how did you know where to find me? I suppose Duncan told you. I'm very happy here, you know. You don't have to——'

'You're talking too much,' he interrupted, and pushed her into the lift and pressed the button.

The doors closed and they shot up to the top floor where he led her into a magnificent suite that overlooked the ocean. He closed the door behind him, then as an afterthought locked it.

'Why are you doing that?' she asked.

'Because I want to talk to you alone and the maids have a habit of barging in.'

'You look marvellous,' she said in an attempt to be prosaic. 'You're walking and——'

'Running and jumping and swimming!' He strode over and put his hands on her shoulders. 'But none of it means a damned thing if I can't do it with you.'

Laura knew definitely that this was a dream. A most vividly realistic one, but a dream nonetheless.

'Well?' he demanded. 'Aren't you going to say something?'

'I don't know what to say.'

He searched her face intently and then sighed. 'I can't blame you for that. When I remember the things I said to you ... But that's over, thank God. At last I can be truthful. I love you,' he said violently. 'I've been rehearsing for weeks what I was going to say to you when we met, but now I'm here, I can't remember a single word. All I want is to hold you close, to breathe in the scent of you.' He drew her into his arms and rubbed his cheek against hers. 'I love you,' he repeated, and sought her mouth with his.

In his kiss there was a longing Laura had never believed she would feel from him; a depth of desire allied to a depth of tenderness that set her body trembling as much as his. Her lips parted and she felt him take possession of her, his hands moving across her back to pull her body still closer. His heart was hammering loudly and she could feel its vibration against her breasts, while his trembling ceased and his body stiffened with desire.

'Laura,' he said thickly, and suddenly pushed her away from him. His cheeks were flushed and beads of sweat marked his upper lip. 'I've got to talk to you first. There are things to be explained.'

He led her to a chair and gently pushed her into it, then he went to stand by the window. The room was silent except for the faint hum of the air-conditioning and Carl's own quick breathing.

'First let's get Rosemary out of the way,' he began. 'When I married you I believed I was in love with her. In fact that was the reason for the marriage, as you know. I've tried again and again to remember when that stopped being the reason. But all I know is that she suddenly stopped mattering to me, and when I found myself thinking of the woman I wanted, she was always you.'

'Why didn't you tell me?' Laura whispered.

'Because I was tied to a wheelchair!'

'Do you think that would have mattered? Didn't you know I loved you?'

'How could I?' He flung up his hands. 'You were such a damn good actress. All cool commiseration and friendliness—never a hint of love.'

184

She remembered the hour on the settee and shook her head in bewilderment. 'I let you kiss me,' she said huskily. 'I responded to you. I was afraid I'd given myself away.'

'I believed you were only sorry for me. Don't forget Duncan had come on the scene by then, and like a fool I'd already started to throw the two of you together. Then Rosemary came back and I turned to her because it was the only way to stop myself from telling you how I felt. You see, I thought Duncan was so much better for you than I was.'

'You're a fool,' she said shakily, and ran over to him. He enclosed her within the circle of his arms and she rested against his broad chest. 'Why did you have the operation, Carl? Surely you must have known I wouldn't have wanted you to take such a risk.'

'I was determined to come to you a whole man. If the gamble had failed, I would never have told you how I felt. I let you think I was doing it for Rosemary because I knew that otherwise you'd try to stop me. You have no conception how I felt the day you came to see me in the hospital and begged me not to go through with it. I wanted so much to do as you wished, and yet I knew I couldn't. You see, I still hadn't realised you loved me. I knew you were fond of me, but I believed it was pity.'

She shivered, thinking of the lonely years they would both have had if the operation had failed. It was too horrifying to contemplate, and she clung to him as if his nearness could banish the horror. 'You took an awful risk pushing me at Duncan,' she murmured. 'What would you have done if I'd fallen in love with him?'

'I *did* think you were in love with him.' Carl's voice was grim. 'And I was all prepared to fight for you when Duncan came to see me and told me you'd turned him down and gone to Brazil.'

'That was six weeks ago!' she cried. 'You let me go through six weeks of misery.'

'It wasn't easy for me either! But I was determined to be completely well before I came to you.'

Tears poured down her face, but she did not care. 'Why didn't you telephone me? Sometimes I didn't think I could bear to go on living. I wanted you, yet I hated you.'

'There've been times during these past weeks when I've hated myself,' he said bluntly. 'When I think of the way Rosemary——' His jaw tightened. 'But enough of her.'

'Not quite,' Laura said. 'I'd like to know what happened to her.'

He gave a slight smile. 'I had a fine time telling her she hadn't pulled the wool over my eyes. She couldn't believe I'd only pretended I wanted her in order to hide my love for you.' His head bent lower and he spoke against Laura's mouth. 'But I don't have to pretend any longer. You're in my arms where you belong and I'm never going to let you go.' His lips moved backwards and forwards over hers. 'I have a message from Duncan for you.'

She stiffened slightly. 'What is it?'

'He wants you to know he hasn't done anything about getting you the annulment.' Grey eyes sparkled. 'So you're still my wife, and in a short time you won't have a hope of getting our marriage annulled!'

'You will have to explain that more carefully,

Mr Anderson,' Laura said demurely.

'Actions speak better than words,' he replied, drawing her towards the bedroom. 'Come, my darling, let me show you.'

SECRETARY WIFE
by Rachel Lindsay

ura loved her boss, Carl Anderson, but he only saw her as his
retary, and when he became engaged to the beautiful Rosemary,
vas Laura whom he asked to help furnish his new home. Then
aster struck Carl and he turned to Laura for help, offering her the
nce to become his wife – in order to protect him from the girl he
loved! Should Laura accept him on those terms – and would she
er find happiness if she did?

THE MEDICI LOVER
by Anne Mather

nen Suzanne went to Italy for a short holiday with her friend
tro, she hadn't foreseen that she would fall in love with his
bidding cousin Mazzaro di Falcone. And Mazzaro was an
stocrat, married, with a child – and divorce was out of the
estion. Was there any solution to Suzanne's problem?

THE WHISPERING GATE
by Mary Wibberley

vas only reluctantly that Andrea had agreed to help Marco Leoni
pretending to be his Uncle Stavros's long-lost granddaughter –
the had persuaded her that it would be an act of kindness to an
man who had not much longer to live. But Marco's formidable
sin Dominic Faro had a very different view of the whole thing –
no opinion at all of Andrea . . .

TIME OF THE TEMPTRESS
by Violet Winspear

ly the tough mercenary Major Wade O'Mara stood between
e and a singularly unpleasant fate at the hands of African
olutionaries. Thrown together as they were, it was inevitable
t Eve should fall in love with Wade. But even if they ever
naged to get out of this alive, Wade was a married man,
h a son . . .

he rose of romance

How to join in a whole new world of romance

It's very easy to subscribe to the Mills & Boon Reader Service. As a regular reader, you can enjoy a whole range of special benefits. Bargain offers. Big cash savings. Your own free Reader Service newsletter, packed with knitting patterns, recipes, competitions, and exclusive book offers.

We send you the very latest titles each month, postage and packing free – no hidden extra charges. There's absolutely no commitment – you receive books for only as long as you want.

We'll send you details. Simply send the coupon – or drop us a line for details about the Mills & Boon Reader Service Subscription Scheme. Post to: Mills & Boon Reader Service, P.O. Box 236, Thornton Road, Croydon, Surrey CR9 3RU, England. *Please note: READERS IN SOUTH AFRICA please write to: Mills & Boon Reader Service of Southern Africa, Private Bag X3010, Randburg 2125, S. Africa.

Mills & Boon
the rose of romance